S328 Ecology
Science: a third level course

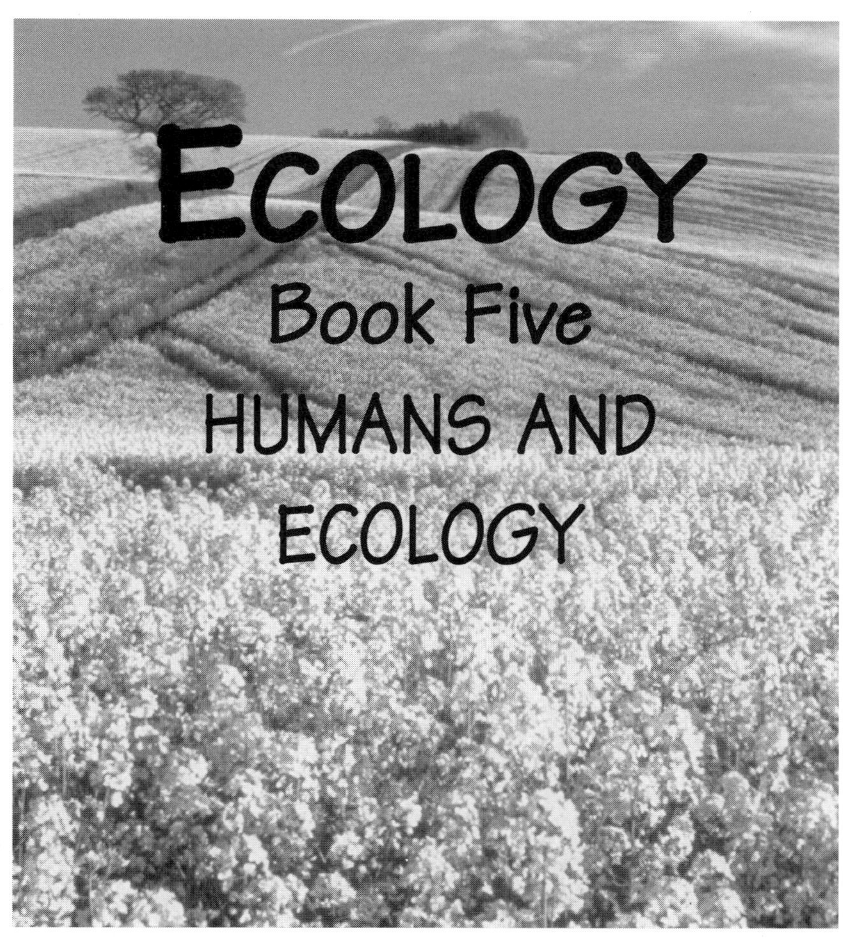

The S328 Course Team

Course Team Chair:	Jonathan Silvertown
Course Manager:	Phil Parker
Authors:	Mary Bell
	Mike Gillman
	Dick Morris
	Phil Parker
	Irene Ridge
	Jonathan Silvertown
	Charles Turner
Course Secretary:	Val Shadbolt
Editors:	Gerry Bearman
	Sheila Dunleavy
	Gilly Riley
	Bina Sharma
	Margaret Swithenby
Graphic Design:	Mandy Anton
	Sarah Crompton
	Jeff Edwards
	Pam Owen
	Ros Wood
Course Assessor:	Professor Peter Edwards
Chapter Assessor:	Roger Smith
Consultant:	Hilary Denny
Comments:	Eric Bowers
BBC:	Tony Jolly
	Liz Sugden
ACS:	Jon Rosewell

The Open University, Walton Hall, Milton Keynes, MK7 6AA.

First published 1996. Reprinted with corrections 2001.

Edited, designed and typeset through Apple Mac/QuarkXPress by The Open University.

Printed in the United Kingdom by Selwood Printing Ltd., Burgess Hill, West Sussex

ISBN 0 7492 51859

This text forms part of an Open University Third Level Course. If you would like a copy of *Studying with The Open University*, please write to the Central Enquiry Service, PO Box 200, The Open University, Walton Hall, Milton Keynes, MK7 6YZ. If you have not enrolled on the Course and would like to buy this or other Open University material, please write to Open University Educational Enterprises Ltd, 12 Cofferidge Close, Stony Stratford, Milton Keynes, MK11 1BY, United Kingdom.

S328book5i1.3

BOOK FIVE HUMANS AND ECOLOGY

CONTENTS

INTRODUCTION TO BOOK 5

Books 1 to 4 examined ecological processes and concepts across species, populations, communities and ecosystems. In this Book, we are going to concentrate on the ecological role of ourselves, the species *Homo sapiens*. In passing, it is interesting that, historically, many professional ecologists seem to have regarded communities or ecosystems where humans have obvious effects as being somehow 'different', and therefore less deserving of study than ostensibly natural areas. To quote Holdgate (1994):

> '[from an early stage] ... scientific ecology stalked off into the wilderness – almost literally ... the conscious or subconscious aim of all "real" ecologists was to study plant and animal communities as little disturbed by human influence as possible.'

A similar attitude is evident in some of the writings about National Parks in the USA:

> 'As a primary goal, we would recommend that the biotic associations within each park be maintained ... as nearly as possible in the conditions that prevailed when the area was first visited by the white man [*sic*].
> (Leopold *et al*., 1963.)

Even without its racist overtones, we might question the basis of this suggested goal, but similar inferences are surprisingly common. In the UK, the designation of 'Areas of Outstanding Natural Beauty' implies that such areas are important because they are 'natural' and apparently not the product of human interference.

In contrast to this lack of interest in the ecological role of humans among professional ecologists, the general public's concern appears to have grown in recent decades, particularly in Europe and the USA. Figure 1 shows the results of a series of public opinion polls over a three-year period in mainland Britain. Respondents were asked to rank important issues facing the country. One issue was 'pollution and the environment', which we can take to mean damage to ecological processes by human action.

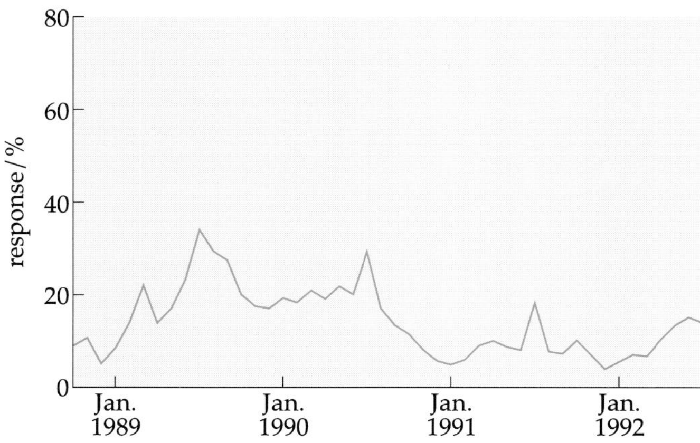

Figure 1 Percentage of survey respondents quoting 'pollution/environment' as the most important issue facing Britain.

From Figure 1, between 5 and 20% of the population in Britain consistently regard 'pollution/environment' as the most important issue facing the country. This is a relatively low proportion, but since the 1970s there has been a growing range of legislation and codes of practice designed to limit adverse impacts of human activity on other species and communities. Legislation includes the Wildlife and Countryside Act, 1981, and the Environmental Protection Act, 1990, in the UK and the European Eco-Management and Audit Regulation (EMAS). Codes of practice include the British Standard for Environmental Management Systems, BS 7750 (1992) and the 1995 draft International Standard ISO 14000/14001 Environmental Management Systems.

After working through this Book, you should be better able to judge for yourself the extent and nature of the ecological effects of humans and to make reasoned recommendations for ways of managing certain ecosystems to achieve given objectives. In Chapter 1, we will examine some of the changes to species, populations and communities that humans have caused, and then in Chapter 2 look at the factors and mechanisms which affect the ways humans interact with other species. Finally, in Chapter 3, we will examine some of the ways in which ecological knowledge can be used as part of the process of making decisions about human activities.

THE RESULTS OF HUMAN ACTIVITY

CHAPTER 1

Prepared for the Course Team by Dick Morris

1.1 Introduction

This Chapter looks at the effects of humans on communities, populations and ecosystems, to give a more precise indication of the nature of human impact than is embodied in the general, and value-laden, phrase 'pollution and the environment'. The first example is a relatively extreme situation (arable agriculture in Britain) where ecological processes are deliberately manipulated for human benefit.

1.2 Local effects: ecology of the UK wheat crop

In 1994, 18 million hectares (ha) out of the total 24 million ha of the UK land surface was used for agriculture. Just over 3 million ha of the agricultural land was occupied by cereal crops, down from a maximum of 4 million ha in 1985. About half the total cereal area was sown to wheat. Cereal cultivation therefore has a major effect on the UK environment. The obvious result is that the 'natural vegetation' that would be present is replaced by a single variety of the single species *Triticum aestivum*. The processes of energy flow and nutrient cycling, competition and succession still occur in a cereal crop, but we try to modify these to suit our demands for grain as a food material.

Book 4 examined the energy flows through a range of different ecosystems, considering the distinctions between systems with predominantly grazing and detritus chains, and the variations in the primary energy input to each system. Human interference in the systems studied was minimal over the periods of interest. Figure 1.1 gives some estimates of the energy flows through a wheat field in the UK.

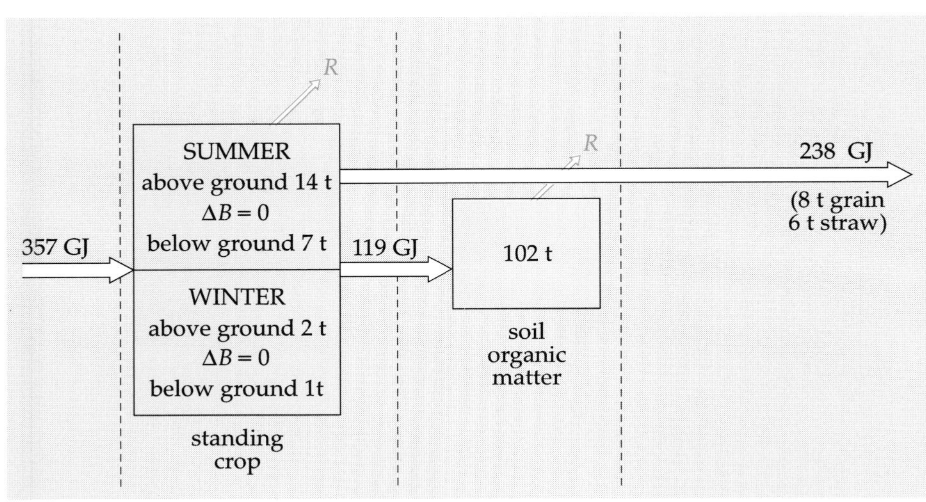

Figure 1.1 Flows of energy in a typical arable ecosystem: growing winter wheat in the UK.

❑ What are the major distinctions between the energy flows shown for the arable field and those of the Hubbard Brook system described in Book 4 and in the relevant TV programme?

■ In the arable system, a substantial proportion of the carbon, and hence the energy passing through the system, is exported in the form of the harvested crop. This proportion is much higher even than in the Georgia saltmarsh system described in Book 4, Chapter 1.3.3.

Figure 1.2 shows the changes in yield of winter wheat that have occurred in long-term fertilizer experiments at the Rothamsted Experimental Station of the Institute of Arable Crops Research in Hertfordshire, UK. Wheat has been subject to intense selective breeding over a long period, and different varieties, with the names shown in Figure 1.2, have been grown in the experiments as they became available.

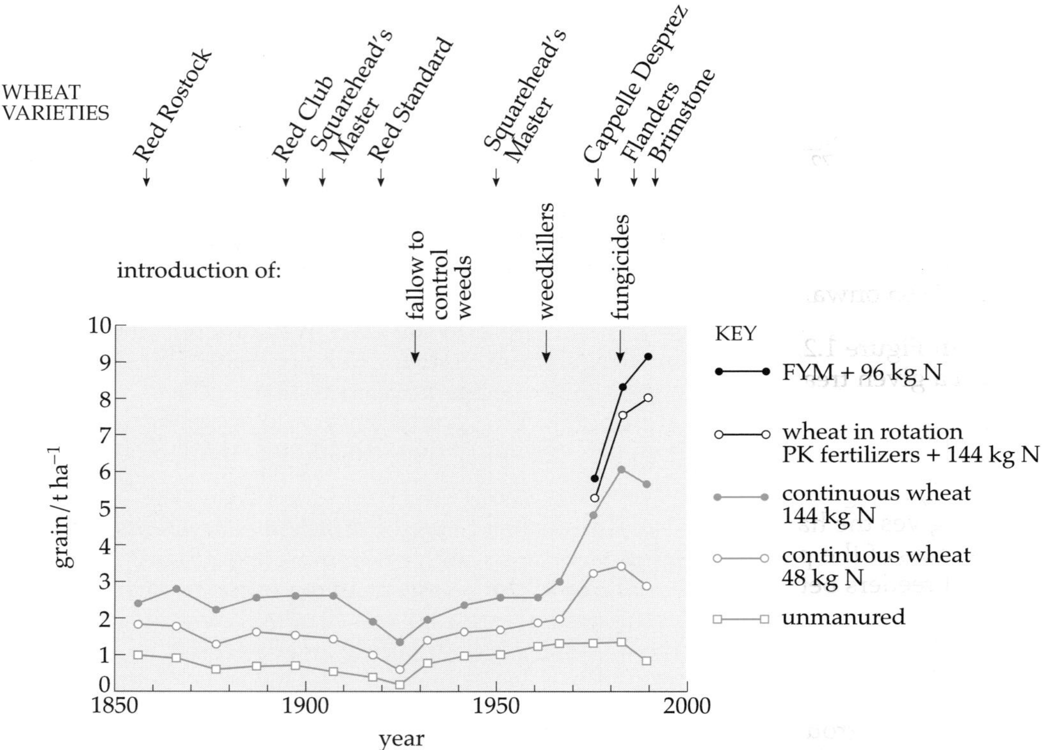

Figure 1.2 Changes in the yield of winter wheat in the Broadbalk experiment at Rothamsted, UK. FYM = farmyard manure; PK = phosphorus + potassium; rates of fertilizer application are per hectare per annum.

❑ Summarize the main features shown in Figure 1.2.

■ Two features stand out:

- the effect of nutrient inputs, specifically nitrogen; application of 144 kg of nitrogen per hectare at least doubled yield compared to the unmanured area.

- the rapid increase in the yields from the late 1960s onwards in the treatments receiving fertilizers.

The response of yields to nitrogen supply is an important feature of agricultural crops in the UK and Figure 1.3 shows the changes in the rate of use of nitrogen-containing fertilizers on wheat from 1974 to 1994.

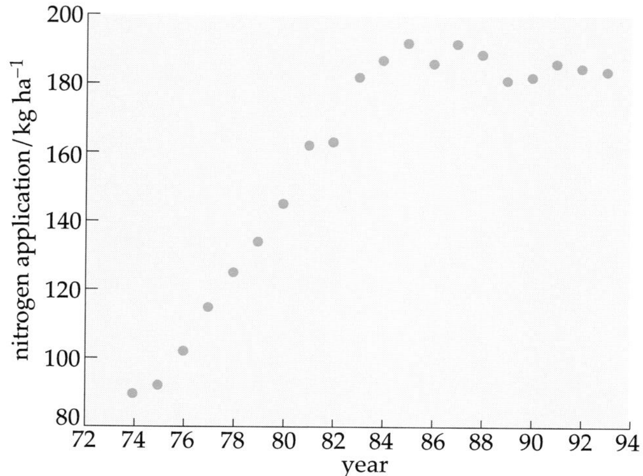

Figure 1.3 Fertilizer use on wheat in the UK, 1974–1994.

❑ Does the increase in fertilizer use shown in Figure 1.3 explain the increase in yields shown in Figure 1.2 for the long-term treatments from 1965 onwards?

■ No. In Figure 1.2, the rate of fertilizer application remained constant with a given treatment from 1852 to the present day.

In a crop plant such as wheat, the harvested yield is only the grain, not the total plant mass. The proportion of total net production (*P* – Book 4, Section 1.1) that goes to the grain is controlled by the genetics of the plant. Table 1.1 gives the harvest index (i.e. the ratio of the grain to total above-ground mass of the plant) for seven varieties of winter wheat, introduced by plant breeders between 1908 and 1980, and grown in an experiment.

❑ What change occurred in the total above-ground biomass present at harvest for the varieties listed in Table 1.1?

■ Total above-ground biomass at harvest is obtained by dividing the grain yield by the harvest index, to give the following figures:

Little Joss 14.5 t, Holdfast 13.8 t, Cappelle Desprez 14.0 t, Maris Widgeon 14.6 t, Maris Huntsman 14.2 t, Hobbit 15.2 t, Norman 14.8 t.

*Table 1.1*Harvest index, stem length from soil to base of ear, and grain yield for a range of varieties of winter wheat *Triticum aestivum*. (Data from Austin *et al*., 1980.)

Variety name	Year introduced	Harvest index	Stem length/m	Grain yield/ t ha^{-1}
Little Joss	1908	0.36	1.42	5.22
Holdfast*	1935	0.36	1.26	4.96
Cappelle Desprez	1953	0.42	1.10	5.86
Maris Widgeon*	1964	0.39	1.27	5.68
Maris Huntsman	1972	0.46	1.06	6.54
Hobbit	1977	0.48	0.80	7.30
Norman	1980	0.51	0.84	7.57

*These are 'bread-making' wheats which have a slightly lower yield than contemporary 'feed' varieties.

Over the period studied, there appears to have been relatively little change in the total plant biomass at harvest. However, the proportion of that biomass which is grain has increased.

❑ How does harvest index relate to the concept of reproductive allocation introduced in Book 2, Chapter 5? Where in the range of strategies for reproductive allocation discussed there do the cereals lie?

■ Reproductive allocation is usually expressed as the percentage weight of reproductive structures relative to the total biomass of a plant, whereas harvest index is the weight of seed alone, expressed relative to above-ground mass. The harvest index values quoted are therefore not strictly comparable, but are clearly at the high end of the range of reproductive allocations.

A second feature of the wheat data is that stem length decreased from 1.2–1.4 m in the early varieties to less than 0.85 m in the later ones. This feature interacts with the use of nitrogen fertilizer: with higher rates of nitrogen use, the stem of the wheat is less strong, and so is more prone to being knocked flat by rain or wind. Such **lodged** crops have a less effective display of leaves to intercept light for photosynthesis and harvested yield is reduced. Shorter-strawed varieties are less prone to lodging, and so can respond to higher rates of nitrogen fertilizer. Wheat crops are often treated with growth-regulating materials to further reduce straw length.

❑ Suggest some possible reasons for the increases in yields shown in Figure 1.2 from 1970 onwards.

■ Two factors shown in Figure 1.2 are the introduction of weedkillers and the change in the variety of wheat being grown. Another possibility is that the weather over this period was particularly good, but this would not explain the continuing increase in yield.

The change in variety from Squarehead's Master to Cappelle Desprez took place in 1972, after yields had begun to rise, so this is unlikely to be the major cause. (The change also occurred at a surprisingly late date, since Cappelle was already an outdated variety by the end of the 1960s.)

The use of newer varieties would allow higher yields, because of their improved harvest index and shorter straw, but these gains would only be realized if the crops were not subject to competition from weeds or to the effects of disease. Weeds had been a problem earlier in the experiment, and caused a decline in yields prior to 1920. At that time, the only method of control was to leave a fallow period (i.e. a period of up to a year when the soil was kept bare by mechanical cultivation). In the 1940s, some organic chemicals, the **phenoxyacetic acids**, were found to be toxic to broadleaved weeds, but not to cereals. These were the first of a rapidly increasing array of selective herbicides. Use of selective herbicides in the experiment from 1960 (some considerable time after they had been used extensively in commercial agriculture) was a major factor in increasing yields. Later increases were associated with new varieties, and with the introduction of effective fungicides for disease control. By the end of the 1980s, economic conditions in the UK dictated that herbicides, fungicides and insecticides were extensively used in cereal crops.

The effects of variation in the use of these materials can be seen in a series of experiments set up in 1982 at Boxworth in Cambridgeshire. Three different management regimes were imposed: full insurance, supervised and integrated. These represented differing degrees of control of weeds, pests and diseases.

The philosophy of the 'full insurance' treatment was to:

> 'identify all those pests, weeds and diseases likely to occur at Boxworth, and to apply a pesticide in anticipation of the need for control.'
> (Greig-Smith *et al.*, 1992)

In the 'supervised' treatments, use of pesticides was based on monitoring pest, weed and disease levels in the crop and treating only when these reached agreed thresholds. In the 'integrated' treatment, pest and disease problems were controlled by changing the crop variety, cultivation etc., and only spraying when monitoring indicated that this was necessary. The number of applications of different pesticides (insecticides, herbicides and fungicides) in the three treatments is summarized in Table 1.2.

Table 1.2 Pesticide use (number of applications) in fields under the three treatments during the five years of the project. (Data from Greig-Smith and Hardy, 1992.)

	Insecticides	Herbicides	Fungicides	Total
full insurance:				
planned*	7.0	7.0	5.0	19.0
achieved*	5.2	5.2	4.0	14.4
supervised	0.8	3.4	2.6	6.8
integrated	0.9	2.8	2.4	6.1

*The planned level of pesticide use was not achieved, usually due to problems of access during bad weather.

The data give some insight as to which of the three sets of pests (insects, weeds or fungi) were regarded by the experimenters as important in reducing crop yields. They allowed relatively small reductions in the use of both herbicides and fungicides in the integrated and supervised, compared to the full insurance treatments, whereas use of insecticides was reduced much more. Control of both fungi and weeds was a priority, whereas control of insect pests was seen as less necessary. Table 1.3 shows the mean numbers of weed species found by sampling in July under each of the three treatments over the five years of the experiment, the numbers of species represented in the seed banks and mean yields of grain obtained over the experimental period.

Table 1.3 Mean numbers of weed species found in July in the crops under each of the treatments at Boxworth, and mean yield over the experimental period. (Data from Marshall, 1992 and Jarvis, 1992.)

Treatment	No. of weed species in crop	No. of weed species in seed bank	Mean yield of grain/t ha^{-1}
full insurance	9.2	5.2	7.74[a]
supervised	12.2	8.7	6.82[b]
integrated	7.6	7.7	6.39[b]

Note: differences between treatment means were not significant for weed and seed bank data. Yields with different superscript letters are significantly different ($P < 0.001$).

Figure 1.4 shows the densities of 'wild' species along transects from the field boundaries into the crops under the three treatments in November 1984. For comparison, the typical density of wheat plants was 240 m^{-2}.

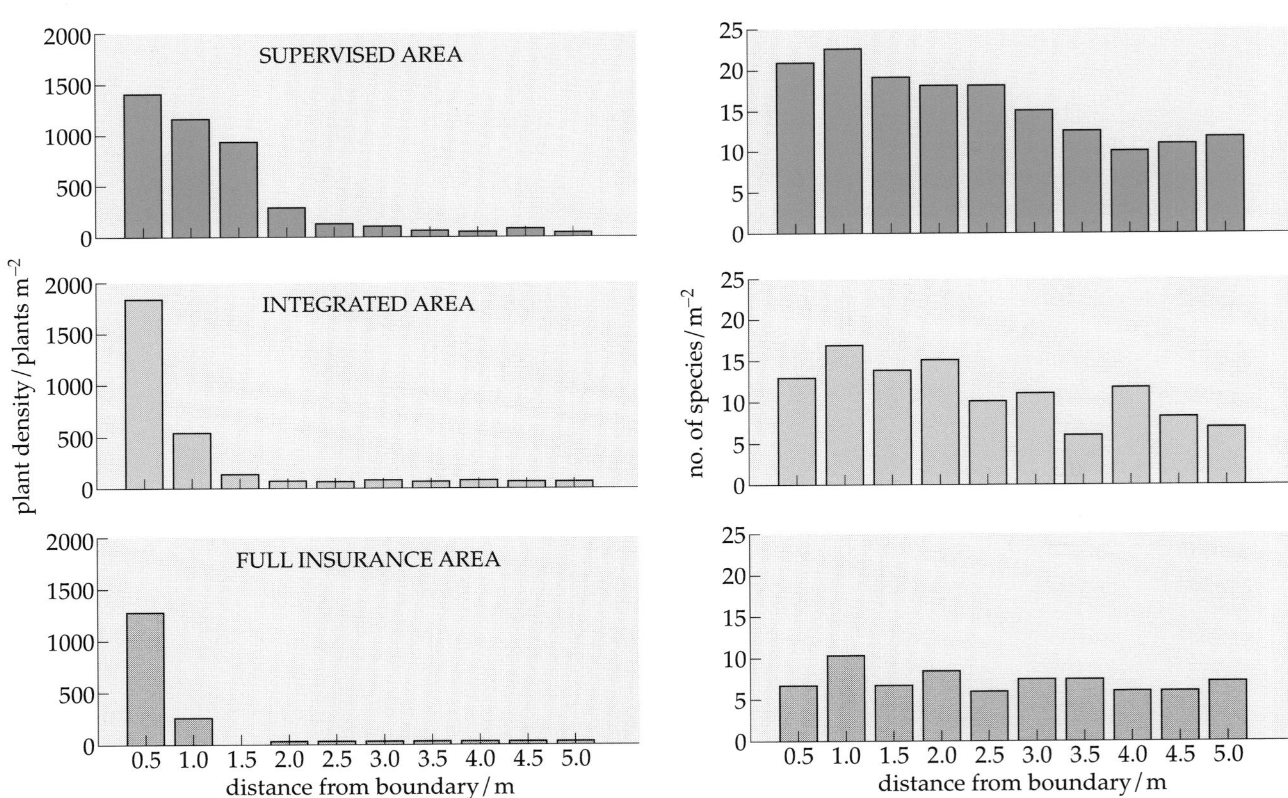

Figure 1.4 (a) The densities and (b) total numbers of 'wild' (mainly weed) species along transects into the crops under the three treatments in the Boxworth experiments of 1984.

These data show that, even under the highest intensity of management, cereal fields are not strictly a monoculture of a single species, and the detailed make-up of the plant community may be sensitive to the management imposed. What is also interesting is the effect of management on grain yield. The highest yield was obtained from full insurance (which at least confirms the effectiveness of the management practices being used). However, the yield obtained under the supervised treatment was such that the loss in income on average was similar to the savings in cost from the reduced use of pesticides. Economically, therefore, there is some incentive to reduce pesticide inputs slightly. Figure 1.5 gives the nutrient budgets for nitrogen and phosphorus for winter wheat and suggests another reason to reduce some of the inputs to cereal crops. In both cases, the nutrient cycles are 'leaky', and the nutrients that are lost may end up in other ecosystems. We will return to consider some of the implications of this in Section 3 of this Chapter, but political and economic factors have already caused changes in cereal production.

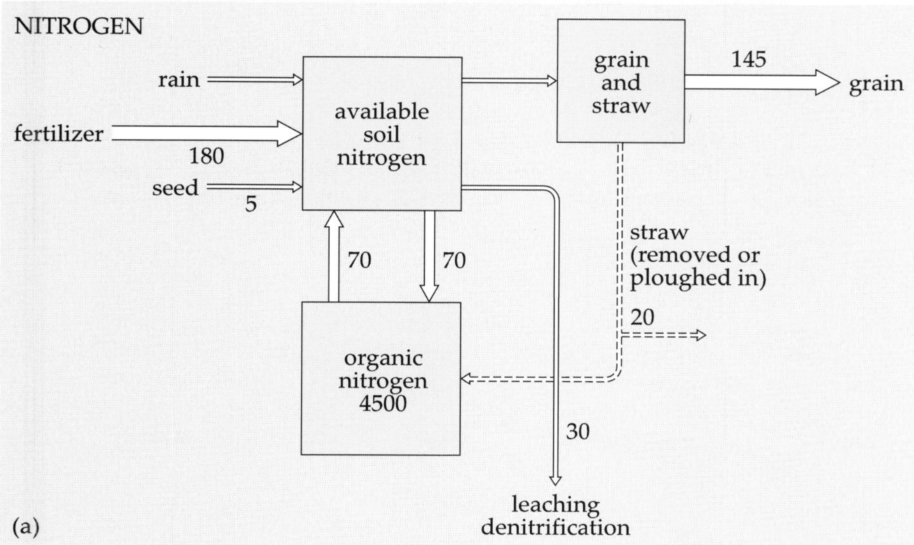

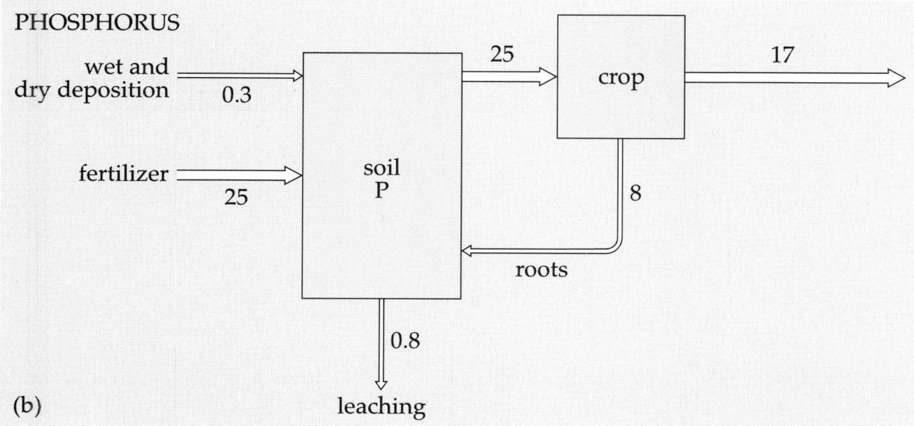

Figure 1.5 The nitrogen and phosphorus cycles of a typical winter wheat system. Stored quantities are in kg ha^{-1}, flows in kg ha^{-1} y^{-1}.

In the late 1980s, Europe was producing more cereals than were being consumed, leading to the infamous 'mountains' of grain in **intervention storage**. To reduce production, the **European Common Agricultural Policy** included **set-aside legislation**, which was enacted in the UK in 1988. This legislation encouraged farmers not to grow crops on a percentage of their land previously in arable use. Initially, the scheme was voluntary, requiring farmers to set aside 20% of their arable land for at least five years in return for financial payments. In 1992, it became a compulsory requirement to set aside 15% of the arable area each year, for a minimum period of one year, but in 1995, the area required was reduced to 10% in response to a general decline in world grain stocks. Under set-aside management, an approved cover of vegetation (**green cover**) had to be established as rapidly as possible after harvest, to protect the soil. The resulting vegetation could only be managed in a limited range of ways, e.g. cut at defined times or treated with a restricted range of herbicides. An alternative form of set-aside allowed the land to be used for specified non-food crops, such as biofuels (fast-growing herbaceous or woody crops) or as cover for game birds.

Table 1.4 and Figure 1.6 show the number of species present and the diversity of species in arable fields immediately prior to and after the introduction of set-aside in 1988. Diversity is measured using the Shannon–Wiener index, which you encountered in Book 3, Section 2.5.2. The higher the value of the index, the higher the diversity (as represented by number of species and equitability (evenness) of the numbers of each species present).

Table 1.4 The number of species and the Shannon–Wiener diversity index (H) for the mean % cover values in arable fields that had been put into set-aside management in 1988.

Date	Centre of field: no. of species	H	Field margin: no. of species	H
5/89	2	1.0	5	1.9
6/89	7	1.7	9	2.0
4/90	8	1.6	7	1.2
7/90	6	1.3	8	1.3
5/91	9	1.2	8	1.4
7/91	17	1.8	14	1.8

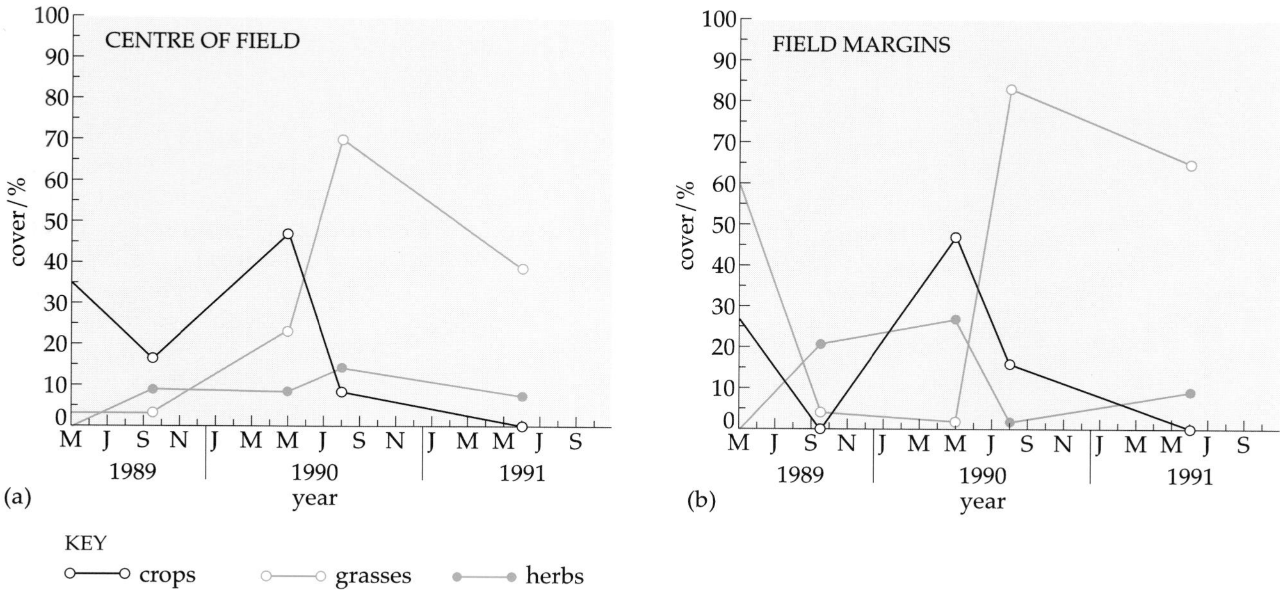

Figure 1.6 Crop decline and plant colonization showing mean % cover of crop species, non-crop grass species and other plants in (a) centre of fields and (b) field margins after the fields were set-aside in autumn 1988.

❑ Which group of species showed the largest increase in % cover as a result of set-aside management?

■ Grasses increased to values of around 70% cover in the centre of the field, and to over 80% on the field margins in the second year. The crop survived for one year, but had almost disappeared by the end of the third year.

❑ What was the effect of set-aside management on the diversity of the flora of the arable field?

■ In terms of number of species, diversity generally increased under set-aside management. However, the Shannon–Wiener index, which reflects both number of species and the uniformity of numbers between species, showed a less consistent pattern, with initially high values which then declined before generally rising again.

Figure 1.7 (overleaf) shows some of the spatial aspects of the change in vegetation under set-aside management.

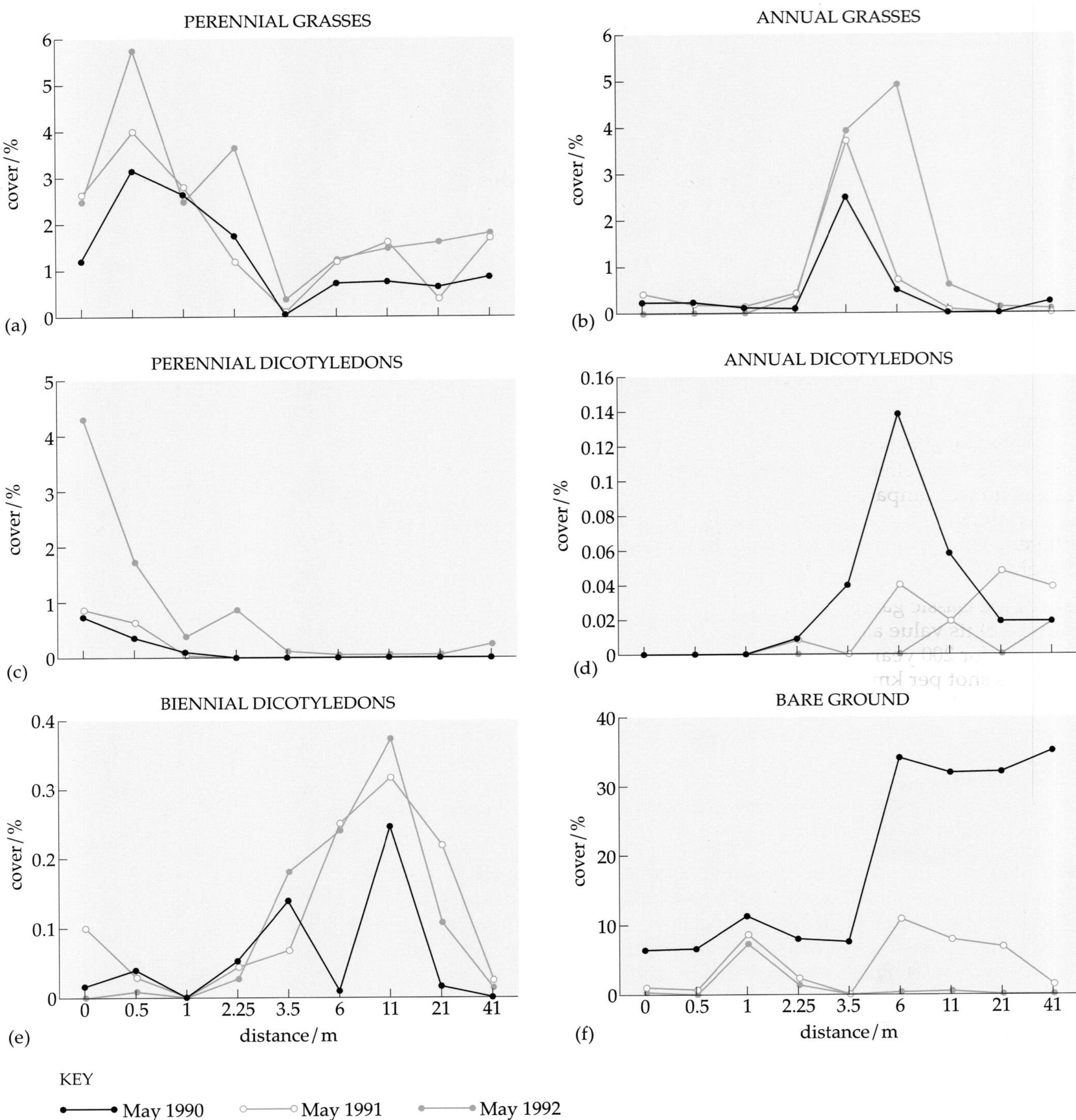

Figure 1.7 Distribution of different plant types (a)–(e) and bare ground (f) relative to distance from field boundary in set-aside land in May 1990–May 1992.

❑ Which group of species predominated in the set-aside land?

■ On or near the field boundary, perennial grasses and dicotyledons were dominant. Further from the boundary, annual grasses were more important, followed by biennial dicotyledons. Annual dicotyledons had their highest percentage cover between 2 and 10 m from the field boundary, but only reached very low cover values.

- ❑ What does Figure 1.7 suggest is the major source of propagules for the species present in the set-aside land?

- ■ The perennial grasses and dicotyledons presumably spread either vegetatively or by seed from plants which were present in the field boundary prior to set-aside. The annuals may have been present in the seed bank across the entire area, but were out-competed by perennials nearer to the boundaries.

Cereal production also affects the fauna. The extent of these effects is difficult to measure, but in the Boxworth experiments, total numbers of herbivorous invertebrates, i.e. those most likely to cause damage to the crop, were about 50% less in the full insurance compared to the other treatments. Predatory insects were similarly affected, but there were relatively few effects on surface-dwelling detritivores. The soil fauna showed variable effects, with total springtail numbers being lower in the full insurance compared with the other treatments, but with some springtail species showing increases over time in the full insurance treatment. These differences were all relatively small, but changes in some of the larger fauna of arable land have been more marked.

One of the classic game birds of the UK is the **grey partridge** *Perdix perdix*. Because of its value as a game bird, records of the number shot (the *bag*) are available for 200 years from some estates. Figure 1.8 shows the average numbers shot per km^2 on the Holkham estate in North Norfolk.

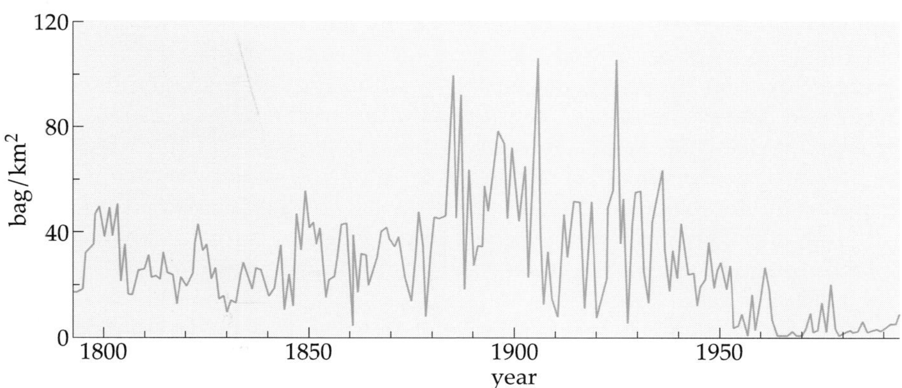

Figure 1.8 Numbers of grey partridge shot per km^2 on the Holkham estate, North Norfolk, UK from 1793 to 1993. (Data from Potts, 1994.)

- ❑ What indication does Figure 1.9 give of the change in partridge numbers?

- ■ The number shot is obviously not a direct measure of numbers present, and there are very wide fluctuations from year to year. It appears that there was a general decline in the bag from relatively high levels in the 1920s and 1930s to lower levels, down to zero in some years, from about 1950 onwards.

Changes in the bag on a single estate could just reflect the owner's varying enthusiasm for shooting or other factors, but the decline in numbers shot was sufficiently general to cause the setting up of the National Game Bag Census.

The number of contributors to this scheme rose from 450 in the early years to over 700 in the 1990s. Figure 1.9 gives the average partridge bag per km^2 for the UK in each year from 1961 to 1992, and the corresponding data for pheasants. Both of these species are reared specifically for shooting, in addition to the semi-wild populations, and Figure 1.9 also shows the numbers reared.

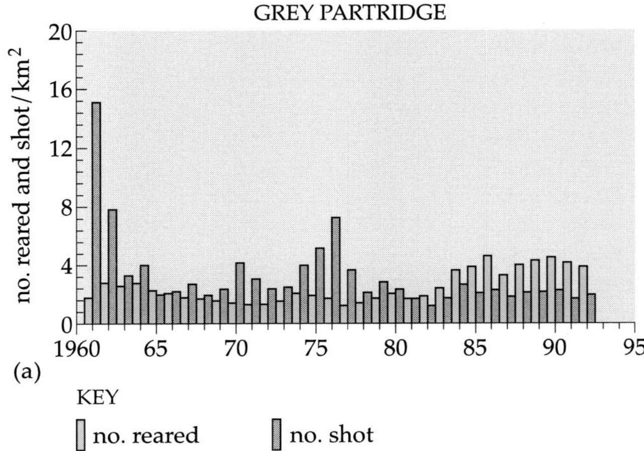

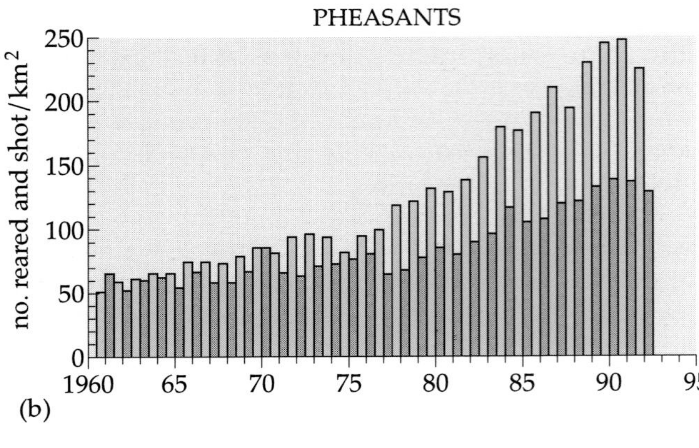

Figure 1.9 Changes in numbers of (a) grey partridge and (b) pheasant shot and reared per km^2 in the UK.

❑ Does Figure 1.9 support the view that there was a dramatic decline in partridge numbers in the 1950s and 1960s?

■ Not conclusively. The number shot is not a direct measure of population, and there are only two high figures – at the start of the series in 1961 and 1962. These two high figures are significantly greater than the later ones, but could be an artefact of particular seasons. In contrast, pheasant bags remained steady over the 1960s and 1970s, then increased presumably in response to the increasing numbers reared.

It appears that there was a real decline in grey partridge survival in the 1950s–1960s, in response to which a long-term study in Sussex, the **Partridge Survival Project**, was funded by shooting interests. Similar changes had also occurred in a number of other bird species (Table 1.5). Over much of Europe, a wide range of what are regarded as 'farmland' bird species have declined in numbers over a period which has seen, in addition to the increases in the use of fertilizers and herbicides already mentioned, a switch from spring-sown cereal crops to autumn sowing and an increase in field sizes, with removal of field boundaries.

Table 1.5 Changes in the breeding population of some farmland bird species in the UK, 1969–1971.

Species	Change/ %	Nesting site	Main food source	Feeding ground
tree sparrow *Passer montanus*	–85	tree holes	seed	stubble
corn bunting *Miliaria calandra*	–76	fallow, coarse vegetation	seed	weedy stubble
reed bunting *Emberiza schoeniclus*	–73	reedbeds, river banks	seed	reedbeds, stubble
linnet *Carduelis cannabina*	–56	low bushes	seed	stubble
skylark *Alauda arvensis*	–54	arable crops	seed, insects	mixed farmland
lapwing *Vanellus vanellus*	–47	arable crops	seed, insects	mixed farmland

corn bunting

❑ From the preceding information, suggest some reasons for the decline in breeding populations of the farmland bird species shown in Table 1.5.

■ One possibility is direct poisoning of birds by pesticides but this has actually been rare. Other possibilities are a decrease in food supply, resulting from decreases in availability of weed seeds and possibly of weed-feeding insects. A third set of reasons could be the loss of nesting sites in trees and hedges and loss of feeding grounds on stubble left over winter.

For corn buntings *Miliaria calandra*, the decline in numbers is claimed to be associated with the loss of weedy overwintering stubble. Loss of nest sites near to grassland feeding grounds is reported as causing reductions in numbers of skylarks *Alauda arvensis* and lapwings *Vanellus vanellus*. The introduction of set-aside in different forms appears to have significantly increased the numbers of these and other 'farmland' species (Wilson *et al*., 1995).

skylark

Summary of Section 1.2

- Arable agriculture affects a substantial proportion of the land surface of the UK, with winter cereals forming a major component.
- Cereal ecosystems exhibit large removal of biomass, and leakage of nutrients from the system.
- To enable large harvested yields, cereals have been selected to show particular growth and life-history patterns. Cereal fields have received increasing rates of fertilizers, herbicides and fungicides. Insecticides are also used, but to a lesser extent. It is possible that rates of use of all these inputs could be reduced slightly without economic loss to the operator.
- Cereal field communities are dominated by the desired crop, but also contain a number of other plant species. The exact mix of species present varies spatially, and with the nature of the management imposed on the crop. The introduction of set-aside management can cause large changes in the communities.

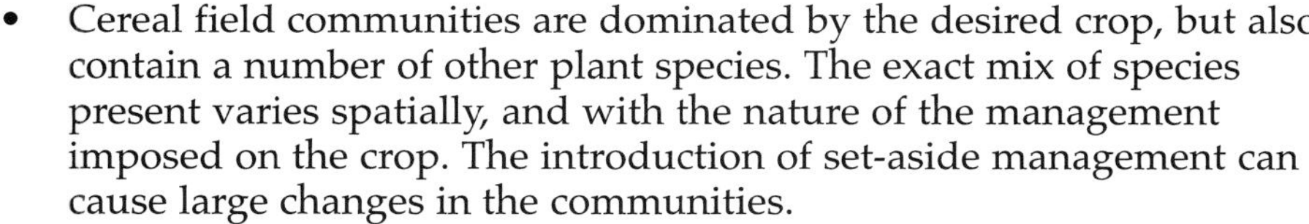

- The birds of cereal field communities were particularly affected by crop management practices over the past 30 years, with many species showing large declines in numbers until the introduction of set-aside at the end of the 1980s.

lapwing

Question 1.1 *(Objectives 1.1 & 1.6)*

Summarize the direct and indirect effects on the ecology of farmland areas that have occurred as a result of the changing methods of cereal production seen in the UK since the 1950s.

Question 1.2 *(Objective 1.1)*

The wheat varieties Brock and Brimstone were introduced in 1985, and in an experiment over a three-year period, their grain yields were equivalent to 9.57 and 9.65 t ha^{-1} respectively. Their harvest indices were 0.52 and 0.49. Are these values consistent with historic trends in these variables?

Question 1.3

(Objective 1.1)

Table 1.6 shows the effect of changes in management on the yield of grain obtained from winter wheat (variety Norman) in three harvest years in Northern Ireland. Describe briefly the main features of these results, and discuss their implications for methods of growing winter wheat in that area.

Table 1.6 Yields of grain (t ha^{-1}) in the control (full management) and differences from the control yield when various management treatments were not applied in each year. (Data from Easson, 1995.)

Treatment	85–86 yield	86–87 yield	87–88 yield
control	7.51	9.33	6.32
no herbicide	–1.18	–0.08	–0.25
no fungicide	–1.44	–2.01	–1.42
no growth regulator	–0.91	–0.52	–1.90
no sprays at all	–3.03	–1.94	–1.25
S.E. of differences from control		0.411	

Question 1.4

(Objective 1.2)

Figure 1.10 shows the peak numbers of seed-eating birds recorded during winter 1992–3, plotted against the coverage of weed species along a 10 m transect in set-aside and winter cereal fields. Describe briefly the main features of the results presented, and suggest an explanation for these.

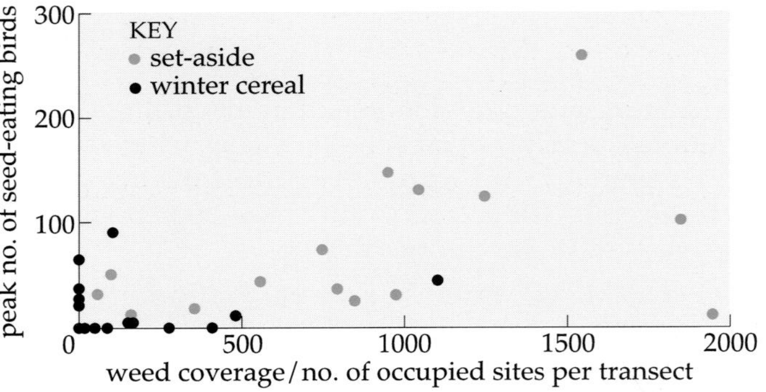

Figure 1.10 Peak numbers of seed-eating birds (finches, buntings and pigeons) in 15 set-aside and 15 winter cereal fields. The difference in weed coverage between set-aside and cereal fields and the regression of peak bird numbers on weed cover were both highly significant ($P < 0.001$).

1.3 Human activity and populations

The effects on animal populations in cereal crops are largely incidental but elsewhere, humans intervene directly to affect the dynamics of populations. We directly control numbers of domesticated animals such as cattle, sheep and pigs and also influence the populations of several non-domesticated species.

- ❑ Give some examples of non-domesticated species which humans seek to influence directly.

■ We try to limit populations of organisms that we define as pests, pathogens or weeds. In addition, some non-domestic species are exploited for food or for raw materials.

Fisheries provide some of the best-documented examples of the direct effect of humans on wild populations, with data over long periods for the catches obtained.

1.3.1 Populations of marine mammals and fish

Whales, **cetacean mammals**, are hunted for their oil, which is used in the manufacture of specialized lubricants and cosmetics, and for their meat, which is classed as a luxury or traditional food in several societies. Various whale species have been hunted since at least the 11th or 12th century.

❑ What effect would you expect this to have on whale populations?

■ It is impossible to answer this without knowing more about the population dynamics of whales, but see the following text.

You should recall from Book 2, Chapter 4, that one possible model for the rate of increase of a population as a function of population size is the logistic. According to this model, harvesting of a previously stable population should reduce its numbers, possibly to a lower stable level which provides a sustainable yield. However, the model also predicts that if the population falls to a much lower level, the equilibrium is unstable, and continued harvesting could cause the population to become locally extinct.

The first recorded whale population to be hunted was the 'right' whale *Eubalaena glacialis* in the Bay of Biscay – the 'right' whale to hunt because it was slow swimming and did not sink when killed. Basque whalers exploited the inshore populations of these whales in the early medieval period, and were later joined by Dutch and English whalers, using increasingly sophisticated equipment. By the end of the 17th century, right whales were scarce throughout the North Atlantic. Whalers then turned their attention to the bowhead whale *Balaena mysticetus*, off Greenland (Figure 1.11).

Figure 1.11 Whales caught per boat per voyage and total catch by Dutch whalers from 1661 to 1820.

❑ To what extent does Figure 1.11 give a picture of changes in abundance of bowhead whales?

■ The total catch and number caught per boat are only indirectly related to abundance. The efficiency of whalers in catching whales may have changed over the years or the whaling industry may have turned its attention to other species. However, the declining total catch, and the decline in numbers caught per boat, is consistent with a decrease in abundance.

Further data have been collated by the International Whaling Commission, set up in 1946. Figure 1.12 shows the total catches of three major species of whale over the years 1920–1980.

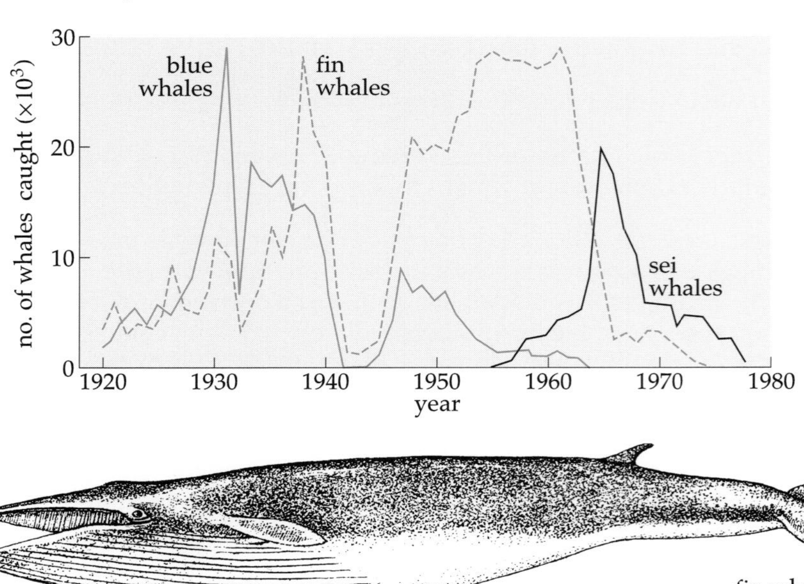

Figure 1.12 The annual catches of three species of whalebone whale in the Antarctic, 1920–1980.

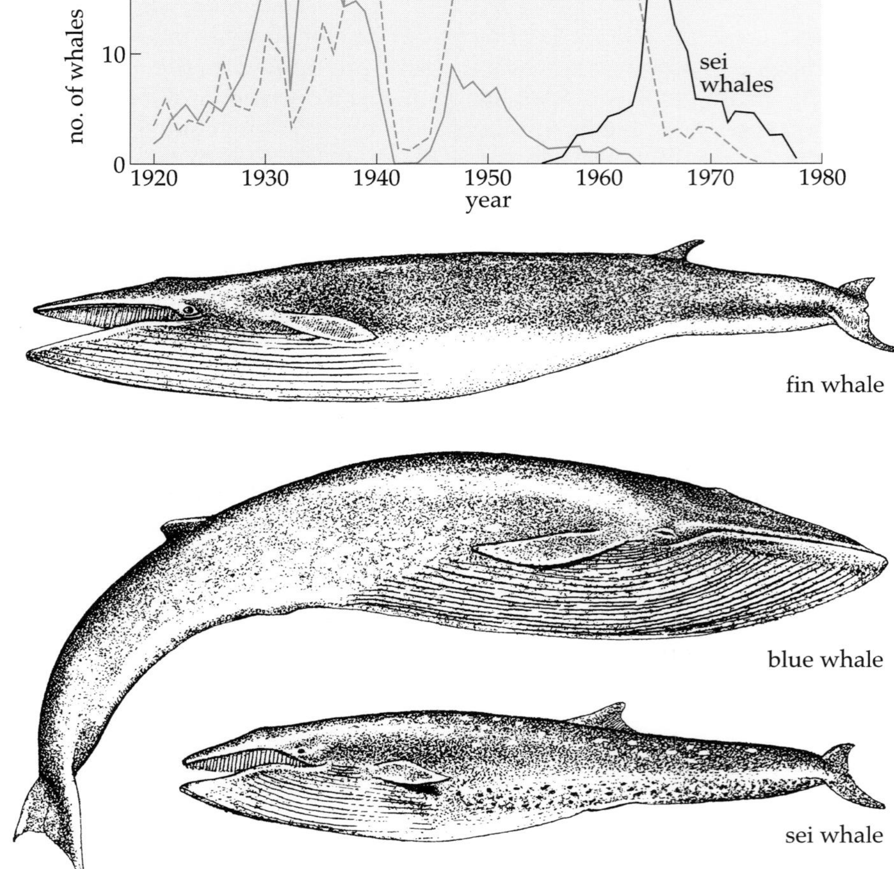

❑ What does Figure 1.12 suggest about the relationship between rates of hunting and the reproductive rate of the whale populations concerned?

■ Again, the data do not indicate the size of the populations, but if a population had declined, its reproductive rate must have been less than the rate of removal plus other mortality.

A more informative measure of abundance of Antarctic whales is given in Figure 1.13. The rationale behind this is similar to that of removal sampling (see the *Project Guide*). To estimate whale populations, numbers caught are expressed as the number caught per ship of a standard measure of efficiency per day. One convenient measure of efficiency is tonnage of the ships, because the more up-to-date and efficient ships were generally bigger.

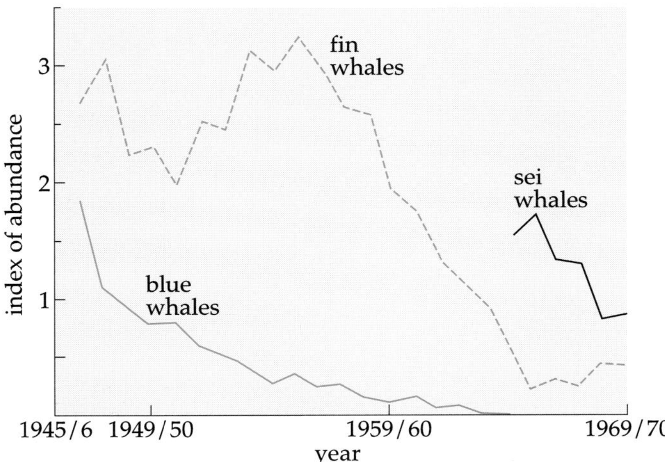

Figure 1.13 Indices of abundance, estimated as the number caught per thousand catcher-tonne-days, for whalebone whales in the Antarctic.

Although Figure 1.13 does not give absolute numbers of these whales, it does suggest a dramatic decline in abundance over the last few decades shown, consistent with the view that all these species have at some time been overexploited. This has been disputed, and in the 1960s it was argued that the changes in whale populations off Greenland were more to do with changes in ice patterns than with hunting. In 1982, largely as a result of public pressure, legislation was enacted imposing a moratorium on whaling from 1985, pending further scientific examination. In 1995, the situation was still unresolved, with pressure from some nations such as Japan for a resumption of whaling.

Question 1.5 *(Objectives 1.2, 1.5 & 1.6)*

Figure 1.14 gives the catches of herring from the Norwegian and Swedish fishing grounds over the period from 1760 to 1960. Do these data suggest that human activity has been a major factor influencing the populations of herring in these areas?

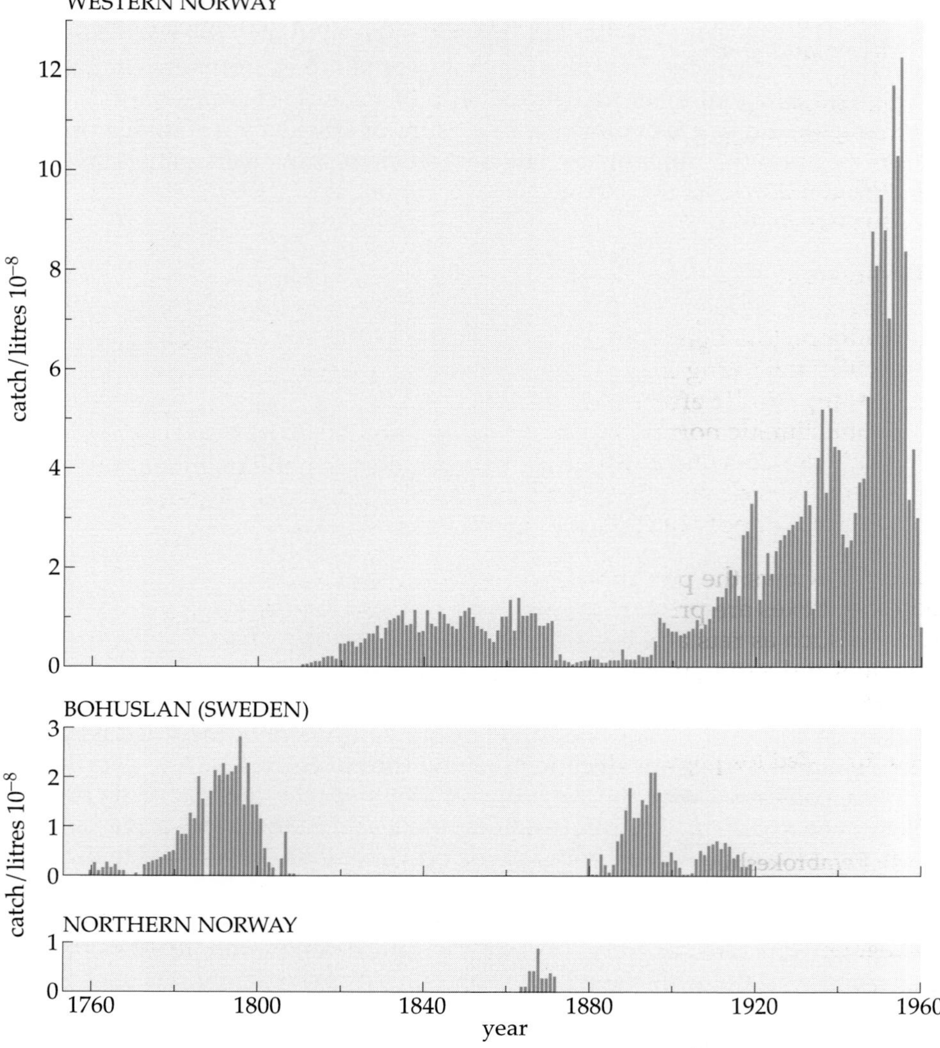

Figure 1.14 Catch history of the Norwegian and Swedish herring fisheries for the past 200 years. Note that these catches are measured by volume rather than weight.

1.3.2 Beneficiaries from human activity

In agriculture and whaling, we deliberately or otherwise reduce the numbers of some species in order to ensure supplies of useful materials for ourselves. However, in the course of our activities we can also create entirely new habitats into which other organisms can move.

❑ Suggest some of these new habitats.

■ Urban areas are totally artificial, with no obvious physical counterpart in the natural world except perhaps cliffs or other bare rock outcrops. The near monoculture of an intensively managed cereal crop has no unmanaged counterpart over a comparable area. However, mineral workings could be regarded as landslips on a grand scale, just as reservoirs and canals are not very different from geologically formed lakes and rivers.

Urban areas are probably the most extreme new habitat created by humans, but even these can be exploited by other species.

❑ What features of urban areas could affect the range of organisms able to survive there?

■ Moisture is likely to be a major factor – the non-porous surfaces and effective drainage provide a very hostile environment for higher plants. Indoors, low light levels would normally limit plant growth, but artificial lighting may be of sufficient intensity to produce **photoperiodic effects**. The temperature within buildings will differ from climatic norms, and buildings also raise outdoor temperatures. Building sites and gardens provide temporary habitats for **ruderal** species which we often regard as weeds, and human litter can offer a plentiful supply of food for omnivorous animals.

Table 1.7 shows the populations of red fox *Vulpes vulpes* in different habitats. Foxes are primarily carnivores, and feed at least partially on rodents such as rats and mice. They are also reported as scavenging in dustbins and eating berries and other fruit. Directly or indirectly, urban wastes should provide foxes with a more than adequate supply of food.

Table 1.7 Red fox populations in various areas of the UK.

Area	**Type**	**Adults per km^2**
North Pembrokeshire	rural, unwooded	3.70
New Forest	rural, wooded	0.75
Hillingdon, West London	75% built up	2.60
Bristol	mixed urban	8.50

Harris (1981) examined some of the factors which might regulate fox numbers in Bristol: Figure 1.15 shows the distribution of foxes, stray dogs and stray cats in Bristol; Table 1.8 gives the correlation between fox density and various factors; and Table 1.9 gives the causes of death of young fox cubs for the same area.

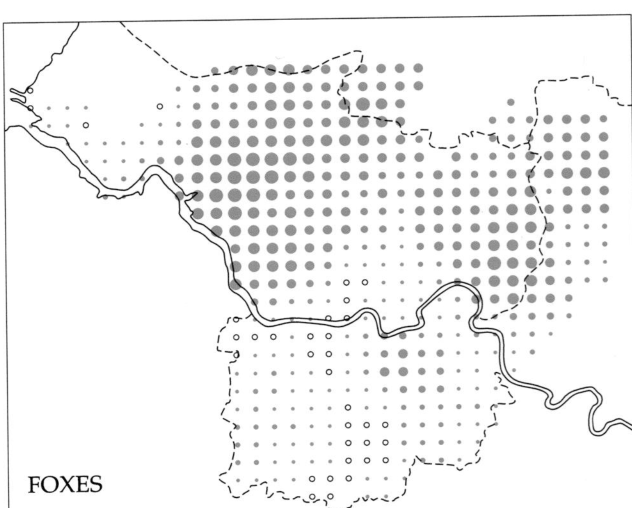

KEY

FOXES

<0.5 · 0.5–1.0 · 1.0–1.5 · 1.5–2.0 · 2.0–3.0 · 3.0–4.0 · 4.0–5.0 fox family groups

STRAY CATS AND DOGS

0 · 1–5 · 6–10 · 11–20 · 21–30 · >31 animals found

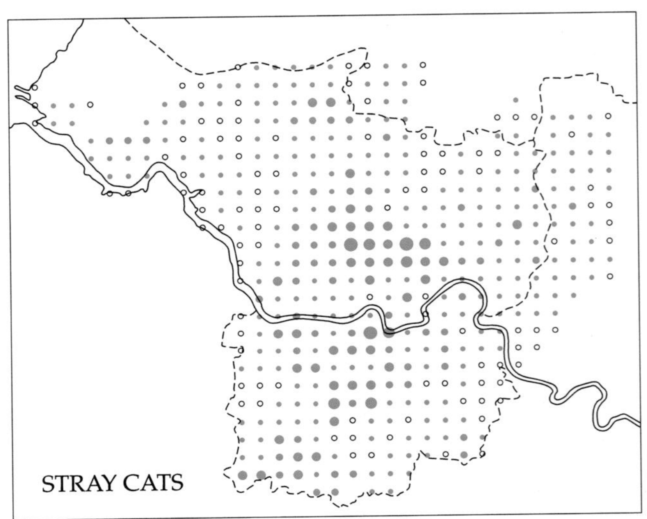

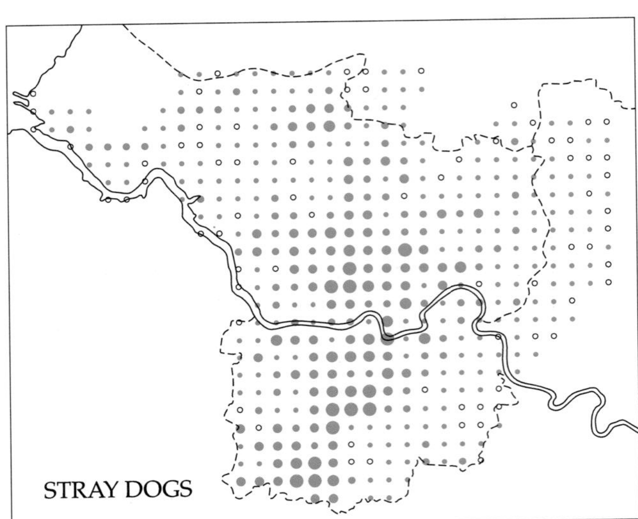

Figure 1.15 Distribution of three species (foxes, cats and dogs) in Bristol, 1977–80. Each symbol refers to an area 500 m × 500 m.

Table 1.8 Correlation data (using Spearman's rank correlation coefficient) for fox density and various other factors.

Factor	Rank correlation coefficient	No. of samples	*P*
foxes vs. stray dog density	–0.300	464	<0.001
foxes vs. housing density	–0.044	452	n.s.
stray dogs vs. housing density	0.322	452	<0.001
stray dogs vs. stray cats	0.682	464	<0.001
foxes vs. Local Authority housing	–0.374	464	<0.001

Table 1.9 Causes of young fox cub mortality in Bristol 1978–80 (87 animals).

Cause	Number	%
road deaths	51	58.6
killed by animals, usually dogs	13	14.9
killed by humans	6	6.9
hit by train	1	1.2
other accidents	4	4.6
unknown	12	13.8

❑ From the data presented, what is the best-supported hypothesis about the factor regulating fox density in Bristol?

■ Recall from Book 2 that a regulating factor must be **density-dependent**. Although road accidents are the main cause of mortality among cubs, this is unlikely to represent a density-dependent factor, unless the proportion of cubs moving increases as density increases. Dogs are the second most important cause of mortality, and this form of predation might well be density-dependent. Supporting evidence is the strong negative correlation between dog and fox density. Predation on cubs by stray dogs appears to be the most likely regulating factor.

The data suggest that fox numbers are unaffected by housing density: presumably any increased disturbance is balanced by the increased availability of food. The negative correlation with Local Authority housing ownership is intriguing. Harris suggested that this was an effect of the higher density of stray dogs among Local Authority housing (rank correlation 0.160, $P < 0.001$). On balance, however, foxes have benefited from the food-rich habitat that has been created by human activity.

Another way in which humans have provided new habitats for some species is by transporting them to areas where they have no natural predators. Table 1.10 shows the numbers of endemic, non-endemic native and established alien species in New Zealand.

❑ From earlier Books in the Course, recall another example of humans introducing species into new habitats.

■ The rabbit *Oryctolagus cuniculus*, as described in Book 1, Chapter 1, was introduced as a semi-domesticated species into the British Isles in the 11th century. Despite the presence of predators such as foxes, it established successfully and maintained high populations until the introduction of the myxoma virus.

Table 1.10 Numbers of endemic, non-endemic native and established alien species in major groups in New Zealand.

Group	Endemics	Non-endemic native	Established aliens
dicotyledons	1463	128	1199
monocotyledons	473	148	380
conifers	24	0	24
ferns, etc.	106	107	20
land mammals	2	–	34
resident landbirds	60	17	33
breeding seabirds	29	40	–
reptiles	60	0	1
amphibians	4	–	2
freshwater fish	23	4	20
insects*	18 000	500	1500

*All data for insects are approximate.

Question 1.6

(*Objective 1.6*)

From Table 1.10, for which group of species in New Zealand is the proportion of introduced aliens greatest relative to the native population? Suggest some reasons why this group might be the most successful invaders.

Summary of Section 1.3

- Humans have deliberately exploited various wild populations as sources of food or raw materials. This has generally reduced the numbers in these populations compared to the unexploited population.
- Simple models of population dynamics (Book 2) suggest that exploitation of a population could result in the population stabilizing at the lower level. Continued exploitation could reduce the population to an unstable equilibrium.
- On the basis of the available records, the rate of removal by humans has been higher than that which might be sustainable for a range of marine species.
- Humans have extensively modified the available habitats for other species. This modification has eventually reduced the populations of some species (such as the farmland birds considered in Section 1.2) but other species have been able to exploit human-created habitats very effectively.

1.4 Longer-term effects of human activity on species

The preceding Sections have shown how in the short and medium term, humans can have a major effect on communities and populations. These effects could also lead to irreversible changes in the longer term, through **species extinctions**. Historically, humans have been blamed directly for the extinction of several species, for instance by deliberately killing the remaining individuals in small populations. Examples within historical time include the dodo *Raphus cucullatus*, a large flightless bird of the pigeon family endemic to the adjacent islands of Mauritius and Réunion, which was hunted for its meat and eggs by sailors landing there. The last recorded dodo was killed in 1681. A similar fate befell the great auk *Pinguinus impennis*, where the last known specimen was, ironically, killed for collectors in 1844.

dodo

For these species, humans were the **proximate cause** of extinction, that is the 'last straw' for an already small population. However, such cases represent only a tiny handful of extinctions relative to the total of between 5 and 30 million species which are believed to exist on the Earth. Alternatively, humans could also be the **ultimate cause** of extinctions, i.e. the reason for populations of species becoming so small that the proximate cause can extinguish them.

Species become extinct in any case during the course of evolution, so it is necessary to compare rates of extinction in areas or periods of active human influence with the 'background' rate. Contemporary records of species are fragmentary prior to the mid-19th century, so the background rate of extinction can only be estimated from fossil records, which are themselves selective as indicated in Book 3, Chapter 1.

On the basis of fossil records, it has been estimated that, under normal conditions, 1% of all vertebrate species might be expected to become extinct over a time-span of between 2000 and 20 000 years. This relatively steady pattern of extinction appears to have been punctuated by periods of more rapid extinction at intervals of about 25 million years, which are currently the subject of considerable scientific interest. Assuming that at the present we are in a phase of 'normal' rates of extinction, we can estimate the number of species expected to have been lost since reasonably accurate records have been available. Currently, there are estimated to be about 13 000 species of birds and mammals on the Earth.

❑ What are the upper and lower limits on the number of birds and mammals that would now be expected to become extinct over a 1000-year period assuming normal rates of loss?

■ At maximum extinction rate, 1% of 13 000 species in 2000 years, and at minimum, 1% in 20 000 years. Therefore, in 1000 years, the maximum number of extinctions is 65 and the minimum number is 6.5.

In 1995, Steadman estimated that 2000 bird species alone had become extinct on the tropical Pacific islands of Polynesia in the 3500 years between the arrival of the first humans on these islands and the present. Island faunas are particularly susceptible to extinction, because they are small, isolated populations (see Book 3) but we would still only expect there to be a maximum of about 200 extinctions over the period concerned. This strongly suggests that the rate of species extinction has been an order of magnitude higher than the maximum rate that would be expected in the absence of human activity. For the Galapagos islands, in the 4000–8000 years prior to human arrival in 1535, no more than three vertebrate species appear to have been lost, whereas 21 to 24 such species have been lost since that date (Steadman, 1995).

The World Conservation Monitoring Centre has attempted to compile a list of the species that are known to have become extinct since AD 1600 and those that are currently listed as being threatened with extinction (Table 1.11).

Table 1.11 Species in major taxa that have become extinct since AD 1600 or are threatened with extinction. (Data from Smith *et al.*, 1993.)

Kingdom	Taxon	Species extinct since 1600	Species threatened with extinction	Total extant species
ANIMALS	molluscs	191	354	10^5
	crustaceans	4	126	4×10^3
	insects	61	873	10^6
	vertebrates	229	2212	4.7×10^4
	fishes	29	452	2.4×10^4
	amphibians	2	59	3×10^3
	reptiles	23	167	6×10^3
	birds	116	1029	9.5×10^3
	mammals	59	505	4.5×10^3
	total	485	3565	1.4×10^6
PLANTS	gymnosperms	2	242	758
	dicotyledons	120	17 474	1.9×10^5
	monocotyledons	462	4421	5.2×10^4
	palms	4	925	2820
	total	584	22 137	2.4×10^5

❑ Which of the taxa in Table 1.11 appears to have suffered the greatest proportional extinction since 1600?

■ Birds and mammals both appear to have suffered approximately 1% extinctions in four centuries. Interestingly, insects appear to have suffered only 0.005% of recorded extinctions.

❑ How representative do you think these data might be?

■ Birds and mammals are both likely to be relatively well documented, so such data are probably reliable. The data for other groups, particularly insects, are likely to be considerable underestimates.

Given the limitations of these data, they still suggest that extinction rates over the past four centuries are an order of magnitude higher than the 'background rate'. It is difficult to estimate current extinction rates, but between 1986 and 1990, 15 vertebrate species and from 1990 to 1992, 163 plant species were recorded as becoming extinct. These are likely, again, to give an underestimate of extinction rates, and even more alarming suggestions are that 20% of the 240 000 known vascular plants could be lost between 1985 and 2015 (Lovejoy, 1980). In the 1980s and 1990s, a particular source of worry was the loss of species from tropical rainforests. Wilson, in 1988, stated that

> '... although these habitats cover only 7% of the Earth's land surface, they contain more than half the species in the entire world biota ... the forests are being destroyed so rapidly that they will mostly disappear within the next century, taking with them hundreds of thousands of species into extinction.'

Although such statements are a useful spur to action on what is certainly a serious problem, you should pause and consider some of the assumptions that underlie it.

❑ Suggest some possible sources of uncertainty affecting this quote.

■ Recall from the TV programme 'The Big Picture' the difficulties in determining accurately changes in the proportion of the Earth's land surface covered by a given vegetation type. Other questions that need to be answered are: how accurate is the estimate of the rate of loss of tropical rainforest? What evidence is there that current rates of loss *will* continue (the quote says they 'will' disappear, not *could)*? What is the basis of the estimate of the numbers of species present, and the rates of loss?

Concern over loss of species was just one aspect of the 1992 Earth Summit in Rio de Janeiro. The concept of **biodiversity** has been devised to cover not just the total number of species, but:

> 'The variability among living organisms from all sources, including, *inter alia*, terrestrial, marine and other aquatic ecosystems and the ecological complexes of which they are a part; this includes diversity within species, between species and of ecosystems.
> (United Nations Environment Programme, 1992.)

There are several similar definitions of biodiversity, and it appears in the 1990s to have a central place in the concerns over 'pollution and environment' noted earlier.

❑ From your reading of earlier Books in this Course, suggest some reasons why it might be important to preserve a diversity of species.

■ In terms of the function of ecosystems, there have been suggestions that their stability depends on the diversity of species present, and in particular on specific **keystone** species as described in Books 3 and 4. More pragmatically, it may be worth preserving a wide range of species in case some of these prove in the future to be sources of useful materials for humans.

Question 1.7 *(Objective 1.3)*

Table 1.12 gives the extinctions of species and appearance of new species for mammals in North America during geological periods over the past 3 Ma. Note that humans first reached North America from Asia about 12 000 years ago.

(a) Estimate the average rate of extinction over the whole time-scale, and compare this with the values for the 'background rate' of extinctions quoted earlier.

(b) What evidence is there for human activity influencing the processes summarized by the Table?

(c) What additional evidence would you need to have confidence that any effects, noted under (b), were really due to humans?

Table 1.12 New species formation, extinctions and total number of species present for large (> 100 kg bodyweight) and small (< 100 kg bodyweight) mammals in North America, for various time periods. Dates for periods A–K are given in million years before present. (Data from Martin, 1984.)

	Period	A	B	C	D	E	F	G	H	I	J	K
	begins	**–**	**3.0**	**2.6**	**2.1**	**1.8**	**1.3**	**1.0**	**0.5**	**0.3**	**0.2**	**0.01**
	ends	**3.0**	**2.6**	**2.1**	**1.8**	**1.3**	**1.0**	**0.5**	**0.3**	**0.2**	**0.01**	**now**
New spp.	small	24	57	31	31	23	13	81	17	42	86	7
	large	4	20	9	6	25	8	12	12	17	16	1
Extinct spp.	small	11	46	26	36	25	10	29	5	12	21	–
	large	1	4	0	14	12	5	5	3	10	57	–
Present spp.	small	30	76	61	66	54	40	112	100	139	211	197
	large	5	24	30	36	46	45	51	58	72	79	22

Summary of Section 1.4

- Humans have been the proximate cause of the extinction of some species which were already rare.
- Species extinctions occur in the absence of human action, and the rate has varied over geological time.
- There is some evidence that the rate of extinctions has increased as a result of human activity over the past thousand years.
- This increasing rate of extinctions has prompted concerns about loss of biodiversity, which has been the subject of international debate.

1.5 The global ecosystem: human activity

Human activity is probably unique in the extent to which it can affect ecosystem processes over a very wide geographic area.

❑ What happens to the outputs of carbon and other materials from an arable field?

■ Most of the crop will be transported away from the field, sometimes over substantial distances, before being processed into human food. For the 'developed' world, most of this food will be consumed in urban areas.

The movement of biological products is not just between the hinterland and its local city. According to Peet (1969), the average distance travelled by British wheat and flour imports rose from 3911 km in the 1830s to 9575 km by 1910. The average has almost certainly declined since then (the majority of UK grain supplies are now either home-produced or from Europe), but it still represents a major movement of materials around the world. The proportion of populations living in urban areas is increasing (Figure 1.16). Table 1.13 shows the relationship between per capita income and the urban population as a proportion of the total population.

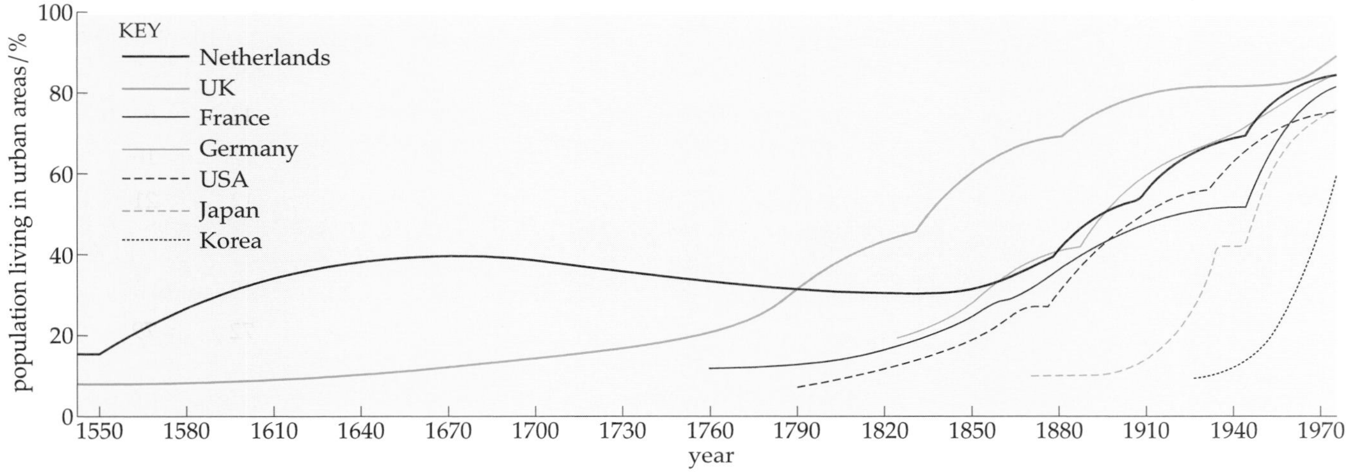

Figure 1.16 Changes in the proportion of humans living in urban areas.

Table 1.13 Relationship between per capita income and urbanization. (Data from Simpson, 1993.)

Type of economy	Per capita income/ US\$ y^{-1}	Urban population as a proportion of total population
low income	320	35
lower middle	1380	56
middle	1930	58
upper middle	3240	62
high income	17080	78

We cannot assume there is a causal link between wealth and urbanization, but the process will probably continue with considerable ecological implications.

Most of the carbon in food eaten in cities is respired and normal atmospheric movement means that this does not significantly affect the concentration of carbon dioxide in urban areas. In contrast, the mineral components of human food removed from the arable areas can have major local effects.

❑ What is the fate of the nitrogen and phosphorus consumed by a human?

■ For a growing human, some is incorporated into body tissue, but for an adult, the amount of these materials consumed will almost exactly balance the amounts excreted as faeces and urine.

For good reasons, urban humans usually have their faecal and urinary products transported away from their dwellings via sewage systems. While other organisms often have preferred sites for urination and defaecation, the geographical scale of movement is much smaller. Sewage is usually treated, by settlement and microbially mediated digestion, to give two components – a semi-solid sludge and a liquid fraction. The liquid is usually discharged into a river system, and the sludge is either dumped at sea or onto agricultural land.

Table 1.14 gives some typical data for the total annual output of nitrogen and phosphorus from a household in Europe or the USA.

Table 1.14 Annual output of water, nitrogen and phosphorus as sewage from a typical household of five persons in Europe or the USA.

Water	Nitrogen	Phosphorus
55–110 m^3	30–40 kg	300–600 g

❑ What proportion of the input of nitrogen fertilizer applied per hectare of UK arable fields (Section 1.2) could in theory be obtained from the sewage from a single household?

■ About half the nitrogen per hectare could be supplied by the use of sewage-derived material.

Population density is 0.28 person per hectare in the USA and 2.0 persons per hectare in the UK. So, spread uniformly, the nitrogen in human sewage would supply only a relatively small fraction of that currently applied as fertilizer to crops in those countries.

❑ Why would widespread use of sewage as fertilizer be difficult in Europe?

■ The sewage is all treated at sewage works, whereas the nutrients from it would be needed over a wide area. Transport costs are high with current technology and there are also strong public objections to odours associated with surface spreading of these materials.

In reality, economic considerations dictate that the 46% of the UK sewage output spread on farmland in 1990 was disposed over the smallest acceptable total area. This was complicated by the fact that sewage from urban areas often contains heavy metals such as zinc, chromium and cadmium, so that as a 'fertilizer' it was rarely welcome, or even usable. Table 1.15 gives the limits on the application of sewage sludge to arable land associated with heavy metal content.

Table 1.15 Limits for the application of sewage sludge to agricultural land in the UK. (Data from Sludge (Use in Agriculture) Regulations, 1989, amended 1990.)

Element	**Maximum application rate/kg ha^{-1} y^{-1}**	**Maximum level in soil/ mg kg^{-1}**	
		pH < 5	**pH > 7**
zinc	15	200	450
copper	7.5	80	200
nickel	3	50	110
cadmium	0.15	300	300
lead	15	3	3
mercury	0.1	1	1

❑ Why do the permitted levels in soil vary depending on the pH of the soil?

■ Recall from Book 1, Chapter 4, that pH affects the availability of cations to plants. Toxic materials such as zinc, copper and nickel are more available at lower pH, so lower limits are set for the permissible levels in more acid soils.

The liquid fraction of treated sewage, with most of the nitrogen and soluble phosphate from human wastes, is discharged to river systems. Table 1.16 shows the nitrate concentration in river waters, and nitrate export from watersheds for river systems in different parts of the world (see Figure 1.17, overleaf, for locations). The authors attempted to correlate these two variables with the area of the watershed, the population density across the watershed and other variables.

Table 1.16 Correlation coefficient (r^2) and probability value (P) for regression analysis of nitrate concentration and nitrate export via rivers on other variables. (Data from Cole, 1993.)

		Population density	**Watershed area**	**Discharge**	**Nitrate deposition**
nitrate concentration	r^2	0.76	0.12	0.15	0.44
	P	< 0.000 01	0.024	0.127	0.000 01
nitrate export	r^2	0.53	0.31	0.06	–
	P	<0.000 01	0.000 13	0.12	–

Figure 1.17 Location of the watersheds sampled to provide the data in Table 1.16.

Multiple regression among these variables showed that population density explained 73% of the variation in river nitrate concentration, and 53% of the variation in nitrate export.

❑ What do these data suggest about the sources of nitrate in rivers?

■ They suggest strongly that human activities are a major contributor, although such correlation cannot be regarded as proving that humans themselves are the source of nitrate.

Figure 1.18 shows the potential impact of human sewage on nitrate export for the river systems studied, assuming that human sewage contains between 4 g and 12 g of nitrogen per person per day. This suggests that the nitrate export actually occurring was in general equivalent to that which would be available from human sewage within the catchment.

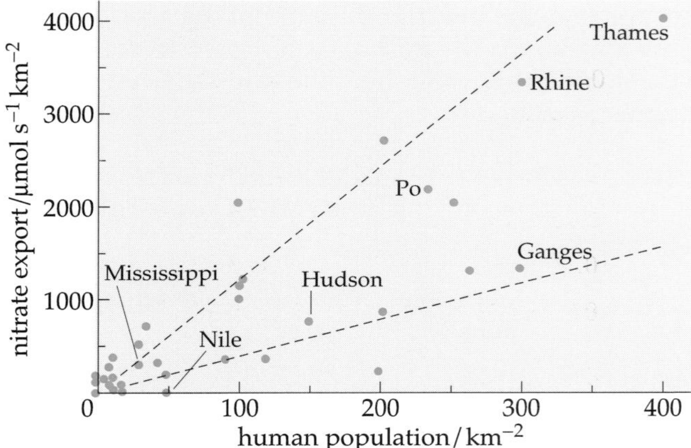

Figure 1.18 Relationship between population and nitrate output from the catchments of Figure 1.17; the limits of nitrate output per person per day are shown by the lower (4 g) and upper (12 g) dashed lines respectively.

❑ Apart from sewage, how else could human activity affect quantities of nitrate in rivers?

■ Recall from Section 1.2 that the nitrogen cycle of arable land can be very 'leaky': much of the nitrogen lost from these areas will be leached away into rivers.

❑ What are the potential ecological effects of increased amounts of nitrate in rivers and lakes?

■ As discussed in Book 1, Chapter 4, this **cultural eutrophication** (an increase in nutrients, particularly phosphate and nitrate) has major effects on the ecology of a water body. The initial problem is a large increase in the growth of plants and algae. Some cyanobacterial species produce toxic metabolites but a more general problem is that as the short-lived species die, the decay processes can cause a drop in the oxygen levels in the water which severely affects some animal species.

High nitrate levels in drinking water in association with various bacterial species may cause **methaemoglobinaemia** ('blue baby syndrome') in infants. All sewage works in the UK are subject to what is called a 'discharge consent', which specifies the maximum amounts of various components that can be discharged into the river system. These will depend on the nutrient and organic matter content of the receiving river, its flow rate, and the other uses that might be made of that river downstream. Such consents are set at levels intended to cause minimal disruption to the river ecosystem, but in 1986, 23% of the sewage treatment works tested were found to be in breach of their consents. This had fallen to 8% in 1990, although this partly reflects temporary relaxations on consents while improvement works were being undertaken.

Flowing water also carries **particulate matter in suspension** or by **saltation** (in effect, a process whereby particles which are too large to remain fully suspended move in a series of small jumps in the direction of water flow). The particulate material may be organic matter, or it may be inorganic particles derived from the soil by **erosion**. Table 1.17 shows the rates of erosion in selected countries from 'naturally vegetated' areas, from cultivated land and from bare soil.

Table 1.17 Rates of erosion in selected countries / kg m^{-2} y^{-1}. (Data from Morgan, 1986.)

Country	Natural vegetation	Cultivated land	Bare soil
China	<0.20	15.00–20.00	28.00–36.00
USA	0.003–0.30	0.50–17.00	0.40–9.00
Ivory Coast	0.003–0.02	0.01–9.00	1.00–75.00
Nigeria	0.05–0.10	0.01–3.50	0.30–15.00
India	0.05–0.10	0.03–2.00	1.00–2.00
Belgium	0.01–0.05	0.30–3.00	0.70–8.20
UK	0.01–0.05	0.01–0.30	1.0–4.50

❑ What does Table 1.17 indicate about the factors affecting rates of soil erosion?

■ One factor is vegetation cover, since the rates of erosion from bare soil are up to three orders of magnitude higher than they are from naturally vegetated regions. There is also wide variation in rates of soil erosion under natural vegetation even across areas as small as the Ivory Coast. Generally, losses from cultivated land are less than from soil which is entirely bare, but the ratio between these two categories varies. China and particularly the USA appear from this Table to use cropping practices which can lead to rates of erosion as severe as from bare soil.

The fate of the eroded soil will depend on the topography of a particular site, but much of it will end up in rivers. In 1995, the annual cost of increased siltation of rivers, loss of recreational revenue and problems with water storage arising from this movement in the USA was estimated at over $5000 million (Pimentel *et al*., 1995). To this cost, the authors added a further $2300 million due to increased damage by flooding etc., and $9600 million attributable to wind erosion. (They estimated that the costs of changes in agricultural practice to mitigate erosion would be $8400 million, which would also save losses of crop yield due to erosion damage of $27 000 million.)

Figure 1.19 shows the changes in sediment deposition in lakes in a number of areas, which gives some indication of the sediment burden carried by watercourses entering those lakes.

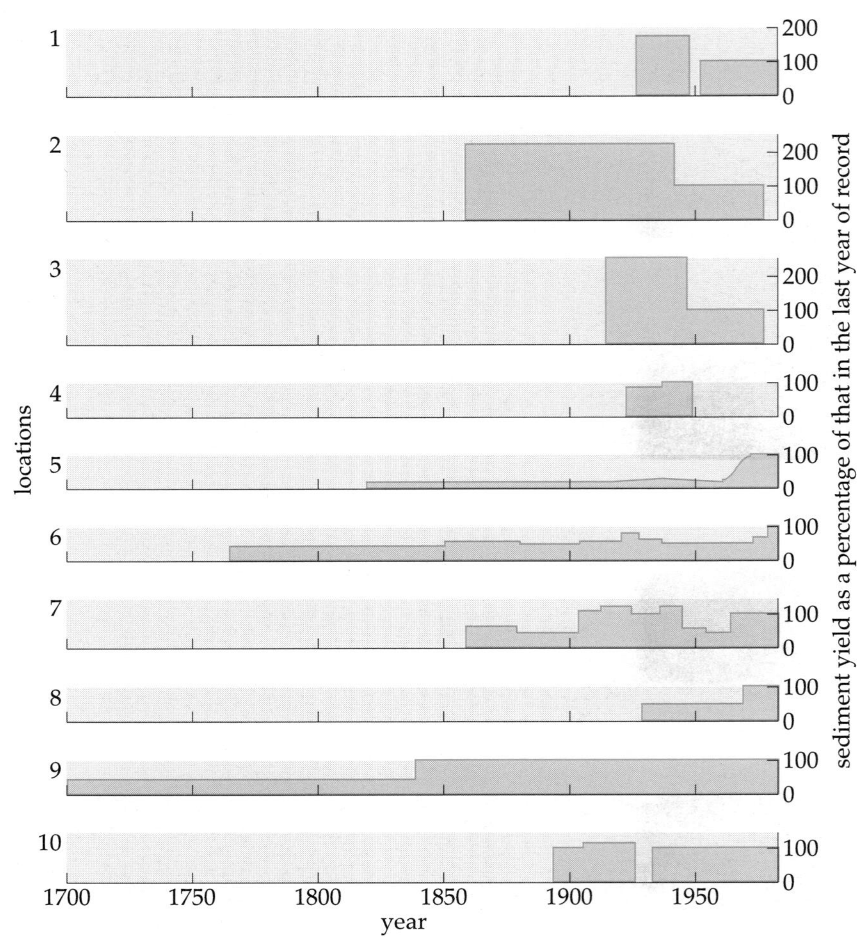

Figure 1.19 Sediment deposition as a percentage of the most recent figures available. Locations: 1 Burrinjuck Reservoir, NSW, Australia; 2 Coon Creek, Wisconsin, USA; 3 Piedmont Province, Maryland, USA; 4 Lake Decatur, Illinois, USA; 5 Loch Grammoch, Scotland; 6 Seeswood Pool, England; 7 Merevale catchment, England; 8 Coombs Brook, England; 9 Llangorse Lake, Wales; 10 Montepulciano Lake, Italy.

❑ What discrepancies are there between Figure 1.19 and Table 1.17 with regard to the UK data?

■ Table 1.17 suggested that cropped land in the UK generally had a relatively low rate of erosion. Yet all the UK examples in the Figure show recent increases in sediment deposition. Some of this may be due to construction work, during which very high rates of erosion may occur, but it also suggests that erosion from agricultural soils may also have increased.

Construction work and the extraction of minerals directly affect the physical appearance of landscape (Figures 1.20 and 1.21). In addition to the local impact, it is interesting to compare global rates of extraction to naturally occurring movements of solid material in Table 1.18.

Figure 1.20 Bingham Canyon copper mine, Utah, USA, the largest human-made hole.

Figure 1.21 China clay waste tips near St Austell, Cornwall, UK.

Table 1.18 Production of major minerals and estimates of erosion and sediment transfer, mid-1980s. (Data from US Bureau of Mines, presented in Douglas, 1990.)

Material or process	Production or movement/ 10^6 t y^{-1}
lime	112
phosphate rock	122
common salt	169
iron ore	795
bituminous coal	2718
natural denudation	33 000
topsoil loss	26 000
river sediment yield to oceans	13 000–18 000

Extraction of minerals such as the first five items in Table 1.18 usually involves moving a lot of waste material as well. For every tonne of mineral produced, anything from an equal mass to a thousand times as much waste material may have to be moved. Allowing for these wastes, Table 1.18 suggests that the movements of material by extractive industries are probably of a similar order of magnitude to naturally occurring transport processes of solid materials.

Humans clearly influence the energy flows and material and nutrient cycles through ecosystems. It has been suggested that:

> 'nearly 40% of terrestrial net primary productivity is used directly, co-opted or foregone because of human activities.' (Vitousek *et al.*, 1986)

This is an impressive figure, but it should perhaps be viewed with caution. The next Section considers some of the uncertainties associated with distinguishing between natural and human-induced changes.

Summary of Section 1.5

- The clustering of humans in cities results in substantial movements of carbon and of other materials from agricultural areas.
- The movement of carbon in agricultural products does not significantly affect the biogeochemical carbon cycle, but the spatial distribution of nitrogen and phosphorus cycles is greatly changed.

- The movement of nitrogen into major river systems is about equal to that in human sewage.
- Local eutrophication of waters results from local concentration of human wastes, and legislation is used to try to control this.
- Mineral extraction results in movements of material on a global scale of similar magnitude to naturally occurring movements.

Question 1.8

(Objective 1.4)

The set-aside regulations in the UK discussed in Section 1.2 included a requirement that a 'green cover' of vegetation should be established as soon as possible after harvest. On the basis of the information in Sections 1.2 and 1.5, give two reasons for this requirement.

Question 1.9

(Objective 1.4)

In 1990, approximately 9 million tonnes of sewage sludge containing the quantities of metals given in Table 1.19 was dumped into the sea around the UK. With the passing of legislation to prevent sea dumping of sludge, this either has to be incinerated or applied to farmland. Using the 1990 limits for rates of application to farmland given earlier in Table 1.15, what area would be required for disposal of this sludge?

Table 1.19 Metal content of sewage sludge dumped at sea from the UK in 1990.

Element	Metal/t y^{-1}
zinc	288.0
copper	147.0
nickel	20.7
cadmium	2.06
lead	129.0
mercury	1.06

Question 1.10

(Objective 1.4)

Figure 1.22 shows some estimates of the inputs of nitrogen and phosphorus into surface waters in Germany in 1987–1989. What do these data indicate are the most important factors affecting the losses of these two elements in this area?

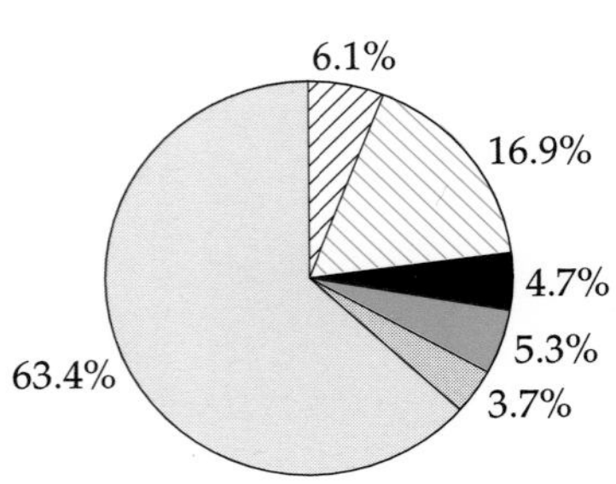

146 000 t N (13.5 kg ha^{-1} total area; 23.7 kg ha^{-1} agricultural area)

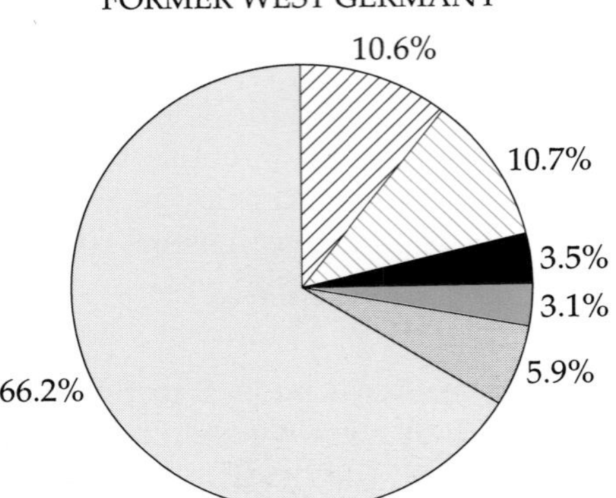

423 100 t N (17.0 kg ha^{-1} total area; 35.6 kg ha^{-1} agricultural area)

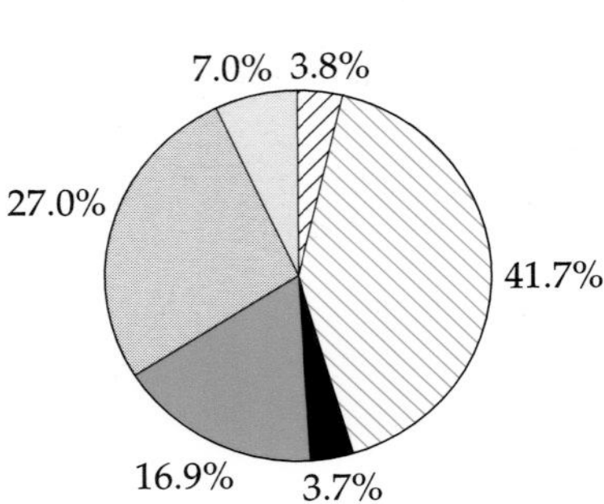

8700 t P (0.8 kg ha^{-1} total area; 1.4 kg ha^{-1} agricultural area)

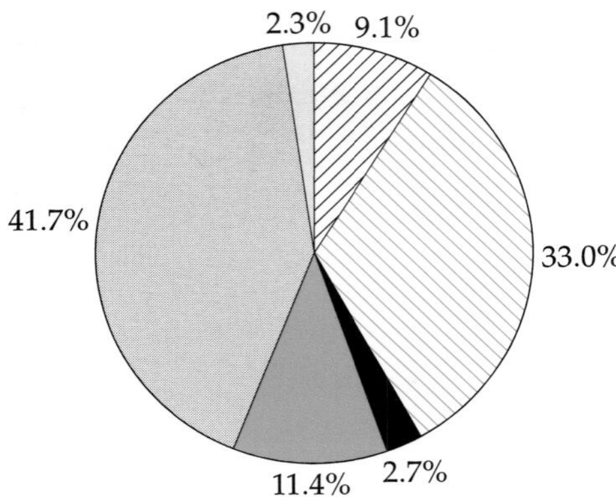

26 400 t P (1.1 kg ha^{-1} total area; 2.2 kg ha^{-1} agricultural area)

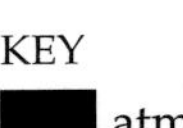

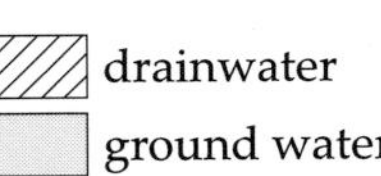

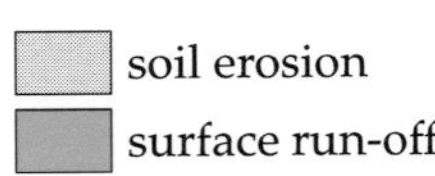

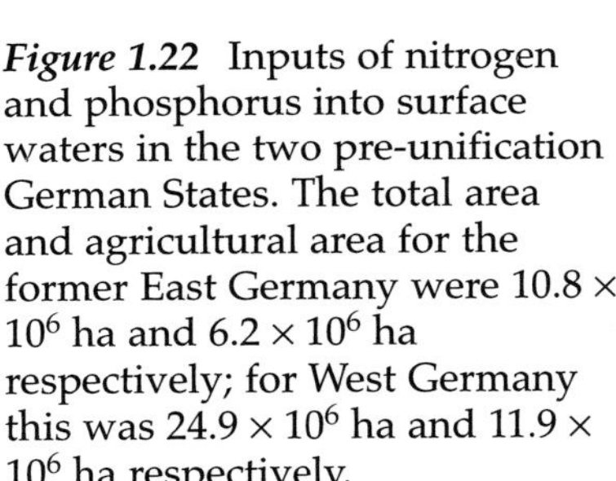

Figure 1.22 Inputs of nitrogen and phosphorus into surface waters in the two pre-unification German States. The total area and agricultural area for the former East Germany were 10.8×10^6 ha and 6.2×10^6 ha respectively; for West Germany this was 24.9×10^6 ha and 11.9×10^6 ha respectively.

1.6 So how much is 'natural'?

Given the extent of human activity, are there any areas which conform to the pristine ideal that the quote from Holdgate in the Introduction suggested 'true' ecologists are seeking?

For arable areas in Britain, the dominance of human activity is clear, but it may not be so immediately apparent in Figure 1.23, which shows part of the area designated as the Shropshire Hills Area of Outstanding Natural Beauty.

❑ Identify the features of Figure 1.23 that are 'natural'.

■ It is very difficult to find many! Features such as hedges, buildings and the vegetation in different fields are certainly the result of human activity. Some woodland may not have been subject to much recent management, but it is unlikely to be purely natural. About the only entirely natural feature is the general landform.

Figure 1.23 The Shropshire Hills, designated as an Area of Outstanding Natural Beauty.

Given this, it seems hard to refer to such an area as in any serious sense 'natural'. But what about areas such as the Lake District (Figure 1.24)?

Figure 1.24 A 'natural' landscape in the Cumbrian Lake District.

Humans walk in this area, and graze their sheep on it, but has this landscape always been like this, or has it changed as a result of human activity?

❑ Recall the discussion in Book 3, Chapter 1, of the history of this area as indicated by pollen analysis. To what extent was human activity a significant factor influencing the current flora of this area?

■ Humans had a major impact on this. By cutting or burning, or possibly through the grazing of domesticated livestock, the previously existing forest cover was removed and replaced by the vegetation that is currently present.

So even this apparently 'natural' landscape is the result of human activity.

Even to estimate the possible extent of 'natural' areas in the world, we need to identify land cover types precisely over the whole globe. The TV programme 'The Big Picture' showed some of the work underlying estimates of land cover for just the UK. The survey of the UK countryside in 1990 used a mixture of satellite imagery and sample ground surveys. Each 1 km^2 of the land surface was allocated to one of 25 or 59 categories for satellite and ground survey data respectively. These categories were combined to give 16 or 17 categories which were relatively comparable between the two sources. Table 1.20 gives the two lists.

Table 1.20 The land classification types derived from the field survey and from the satellite imagery for Great Britain in 1990, and the percentages allocated to different types by the two methods.

Field survey	%	Satellite survey	%
communications	2	continuous urban	1.1
built up	7	suburban	5.5
tilled land	21	tilled land	21.4
managed grass	29	managed grass	27.3
rough grass / marsh	5	rough grass / marsh	1.8
dense bracken	2	bracken	1.5
moorland grass	5	heath / moor grass	8.4
open heath	6	open shrub heath / moor	11.5
dense heath	2	dense shrub heath / moor	3.0
wet heath and saturated bog	7	bog	1.8
broadleaved / mixed woodland	6	deciduous / mixed wood	5.1
coniferous woodland	6	coniferous woodland	3.2
inland bare	+	inland bare	1.1
saltmarsh	+	saltmarsh	0.2
coastal bare	1	coastal bare	0.6
inland water	1	inland water	0.7
		sea / estuary	3.2
		unclassified	2.6
Total area / km^2	231 800		240 222

Although the two sets of data are similar, they are both subject to different sources of error. The ground survey data were derived from a stratified sample of 508 squares of 1 km × 1 km, so are accurate at a small scale. However, to use these to estimate totals for the whole country, it is necessary to know how representative the chosen sample areas are. Your experience at Residential School should also have given you an idea of the amount of labour involved in this sort of survey work. In contrast, satellites provide data for almost every point on the whole land-mass, down to a unit of around 20 m × 20 m. These data comprise measurements of **reflectance**, that is radiation reflected from each unit area of the ground, in three ranges of wavelengths: red, middle infra-red and far infra-red. Each sampled area is referred to as a **pixel**. For each pixel, there were reflectance data for summer and winter. Using the ground survey data to 'train' the computer about the reflectance characteristics of each of the chosen classes, it was possible to allocate each pixel to a given land cover type. Such a process inevitably cannot provide an exact matching between the reflectance data and the defined classes of land cover. You should be aware of such limitations when looking at any large-scale vegetation classification data, and when considering any quoted figures for changes in vegetation types on a global scale.

Hannah *et al.* (1994) made a 'Preliminary inventory of human disturbance of world ecosystems'. They classified ecosystems into three categories as shown in Table 1.21, using a whole range of data sources, including remote sensing, and a wide range of surveys. The smallest mapping unit was 20 km by 20 km. Table 1.22 shows the percentages of the land surface in the three categories for eight **biogeographic** regions and for selected areas within some of these. Note that the biogeographic regions do not correspond exactly to those introduced in Book 3, Chapter 1.

Table 1.21 Definitions and mapping criteria for degree of disturbance of ecosystems by humans. (Based on Hannah *et al.*, 1994.)

Classification	**Mapping criteria**
undisturbed	recorded as primary vegetation; human population density < 1 person km^{-2} in tundra or arid / semi-arid communities, < 10 persons km^{-2} elsewhere
partially disturbed	records of shifting or extensive agriculture, secondary but naturally regenerating vegetation
human dominated	permanent agriculture or urban settlement, areas which have suffered desertification or 90% soil loss

Table 1.22 Percentages of land surface in the three categories of human influence for total area and selected areas in different biogeographic regions.

Region	**Total area/km^2**	**Undisturbed**	**Partially disturbed**	**Human dominated**
Afro-tropical	24 473 218	35.8	45.3	18.9
Guinean rainforest	459 205	7.3	0.9	91.8
Congo rainforest	2 195 019	61.2	21.4	17.3
Antarctic	933 683	98.4	0.1	1.5
New Zealand	297 759	27.1	4.2	68.7
Australian	8 255 821	62.1	27.8	10.1
Oceanian	933 683	77.6	12.3	10.1
Indo–Malayan	87 85 216	11.6	31.8	56.6
Java	153 132	0.0	14.9	85.1
Indus–Ganges monsoon forest	1 859 022	0.1	43.1	56.8
Nearctic	24 749 723	58.2	18.8	23.0
Canadian taiga	5 646 006	88.1	4.8	7.1
Neotropical	21 550 527	59.9	22.2	17.9
Uruguayan pampas	541 199	0.7	79.3	20.0
Amazonia	2 864 623	98.0	0.0	2.0
Palaearctic	59 732 302	51.8	23.2	25.0
British Isles	255 272	0.2	1.1	98.7
Central European highlands	436 364	0.0	26.5	73.5
World	162 052 681	51.9	24.2	23.9

❑ What are the major differences between and within the biogeographic regions in the proportion of land affected by human activity?

■ There are bigger differences within some of the regions than there are between regions. Oceania and Antarctica show relatively less human influence, and the Indo–Malayan and Afro-tropical regions relatively high rates of influence. Within the Neotropical region, there is enormous variation in the extent of human influence.

The global figure of 51.9% overestimates the land surface unaffected by human activity, as it includes areas of bare rock, desert (some of which may be a result of earlier human action) and other areas unlikely to provide useful resources for humans. Removing these gives the much lower figure of 27% of land surface unaffected by human activity. Table 1.23 indicates approximately how land use has changed over recent years.

Table 1.23 World land use in 1974 and 1989 as % of total land area. (Data from *FAO Production Yearbook*, 1992.)

	1974	**1989**
total land area/ha × 10^3	13 073 284	13 076 044
arable land/%	10.20	10.50
permanent crops/%	0.72	0.79
permanent pasture/%	25.41	25.27
forest and woodland/%	32.31	31.25
other land/%	31.36	32.18

❑ Which land use category shows the largest proportional change between the two dates?

■ As a proportion, permanent crops (vines, tea, coffee, etc.) show the largest change, although they occupy only a relatively small area of land. Arable land, forest and 'other land' all change by only about 3% of their 1974 value, with forest decreasing and the others increasing.

Human activity replaced forests by herbaceous vegetation in the UK, and this is a prominent feature of conventional agriculture wherever it is practised. Estimates vary for the total amount of **forest clearance** throughout the world, but Darby (1956) estimated that in AD 900 forests still covered about 90% of the surface of Western Europe; compare this to the current figure of about 34%, much of which is northern boreal forest where settled agriculture would be difficult. The rates of clearance of tropical forest are currently estimated by the Food and Agriculture Organization to be in the range 1.1–1.5% of existing forest area per annum, while Wilson (1988) claimed rates as high as 2–3%.

❑ Using the data in Table 1.23, estimate the annual percentage rate of forest clearance for the whole world during that period.

- The percentage occupied by forest and woodland changed from 32.31% of 13 073 284 × 10^3 ha to 31.25% of 13 076 044 × 10^3 ha over a 15-year period. This represents a change from 4 224 373 × 10^3 ha to 4 086 694 × 10^3 ha, a loss of 137 679 out of 4 224 373 × 10^3 ha. As a percentage, this represents 0.22% per annum.

The figure calculated above is a global average, and it is not possible to say how this relates to the percentage loss of tropical forest. Regularly repeated satellite data can be used to obtain relatively accurate estimates of forest clearance and regrowth. In 1995, an enormous amount of such data was pouring into ground receiving stations daily, but the task of processing and interpreting it was also enormous. As an indication, it is estimated that many hundreds of terabytes of reflectance data were being received per day (a terabyte is a million megabytes and the typical hard disk of a contemporary desktop computer holds around 100 megabytes).

Table 1.24 Human activity during periods corresponding to different zones in the pollen diagram.

Zone	Human activity
I	minimal
II	some European settlement in adjoining regions
III	land clearance and extensive agriculture
IV	farm abandonment

Question 1.11 *(Objective 1.6)*

Figure 1.25 shows a pollen diagram from a swamp in Massachusetts. Table 1.24 indicates the extent of human activity corresponding to the four zones I, II, III and IV. Does the Figure suggest that human activity has had similar effects there as occurred in the English Lake District at an earlier date? Identify any apparent anomalies in the data.

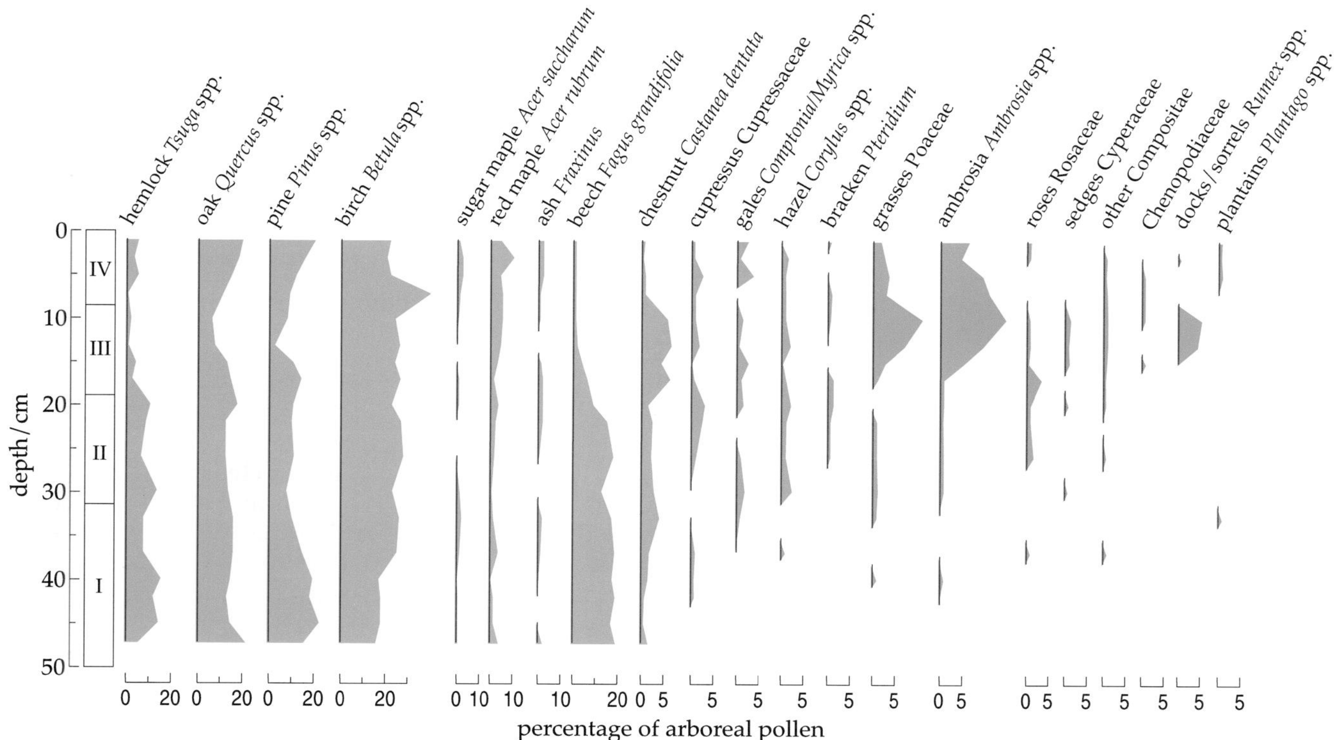

Figure 1.25 Pollen diagram from the Black Gum Swamp in the Harvard Forest, Massachusetts.

Question 1.12 *(Objective 1.7)*

How consistent are Hannah *et al.*'s estimates of the proportion of the British Isles' land surface uninfluenced by human activity and the land cover data given in the Countryside Survey?

Summary of Section 1.6

- Human activity has significantly affected most of the farmed landscape in the developed world.
- Classification of vegetation on a wide geographic scale is subject to different inaccuracies depending on the techniques used. Survey techniques can only cover limited areas; remote sensing has to be interpreted to provide information about vegetation.
- On a global basis, about half the land surface is strongly affected by human activity, but the proportion varies widely within and between biogeographic regions.
- Replacement of forest by herbaceous vegetation is a common feature of human intervention in succession. Estimates of the rates of forest clearance are subject to debate, but are of the order of 0.2% per year.

Objectives for Chapter 1

After completing Chapter 1, you should be able to:

1.1 Recall and use in their correct context the terms shown in **bold** in the text. (*Questions 1.1–1.3*)

1.2 Describe the major general effects of humans on species, populations and communities. (*Questions 1.4, 1.5*)

1.3 Estimate rates of extinction of species and discuss the extent to which these have been changed by human activity. (*Question 1.7*)

1.4 Recognize the importance of human activity in changing the rates and geographical distribution of nutrient flows. (*Questions 1.8–1.10*)

1.5 Indicate the magnitude of human effects on ecosystem processes at a global scale. (*Questions 1.4, 1.6, 1.11*)

1.6 Recognize changes in communities which are associated with human activity. (*Question 1.5*)

1.7 Recognize some of the difficulties associated with estimating the extent to which communities are, or have been, influenced by human activity, and give some estimates of the global extent of more or less affected communities. (*Question 1.12*)

References for Chapter 1

Atkinson, I. A. E. and Cameron, E. K. (1993) Human influence on the terrestrial biota and biotic communities of New Zealand, *Trends in Ecology and Evolution*, **8**, 447–51.

Austin, R. B. *et al.* (1980) *Journal of Agricultural Science* (*Camb.*), **94**, 675–89.

Brodie, L. D. S., Gallagher, C., Hitchin, S., Noel, T., Harris, G. L. and Pepper, T. J. (1992) Spatial and temporal variation in the vegetation in set aside fields at Conington, Cambridgeshire, *BCPC Monograph No. 50*, Set-aside, p.137.

Cole, J. J., Peierls, B. L., Caraco, N. F. and Pace, M. L. (1993) Nitrogen loading of rivers as a human driven process, in McDonnell, M. J. and Pickett, S. T. A. *Humans as Components of Ecosystems*, Springer Verlag.

Commoner, B. (1972) *The Closing Circle*, Knopf, NY.

Darby, H. C. (1956) in W. L. Thomas (ed.) *Man's Role in Changing the Face of the Earth*, **1**, 203, University of Chicago Press.

Douglas, I., (1990) Sediment transfer and siltation, in B. L. Turner II (ed.) *The Earth as Transformed by Human Action*, Cambridge University Press.

Easson, D. L. (1995) The effects of omitting or reducing pesticide and other inputs on the disease and yield components of winter wheat in Northern Ireland, *Journal of Agricultural Science (Camb.)*, **124**, 343–50.

Ehrlich, P. R. and Ehrlich, A. H. (1990) *The Population Explosion*, Simon and Schuster, NY.

FAO Production Yearbook, 1992, Food and Agriculture Organisation.

Gambell, R. (1993) International management of whales and whaling; an historical review of the regulation of commercial and aboriginal subsistence whaling, *ARCTIC*, **46**, 97–107.

Greig-Smith, P. W., Frampton, G. K. and Hardy, A. R. (eds) (1992) *Pesticides, Cereal Farming and the Environment. The Boxworth Project*, HMSO.

Hannah, L., Lohse, D., Hutchinson, C., Carr, J. L. and Lankerani, A. (1994) A preliminary inventory of human disturbance of world ecosystems, *Ambio*, **23**, 246–50.

Harris, S. (1981) An examination of the number of foxes (*Vulpes vulpes*) in the city of Bristol, and some possible factors affecting their distribution, *Journal of Applied Ecology*, **18**, 455–65.

Holdgate, M. W. (1994) Ecology, development and global policy, *Journal of Applied Ecology*, **31**, 210–11.

ISO 14000 (1995) *Environmental Management Systems – General Guidelines on Principles, Systems and Supporting Techniques*, Committee Draft.

Jarvis, R. H., Performance of crops and economics of production., in: P. Greig-Smith, G. Frampton and T. Hardy (eds) (1992), *Pesticides, Cereal Farming and the Environment. The Boxworth Project*, HMSO.

Leopold, A. S., Cain, S. A., Cottam, C. M., Gabrielson, I. N., and Kimball, T. L. (1963) Wildlife management in the national parks, *Transactions of North American Wildlife and Natural Resources Conference*, **28**, 28–45.

Lovejoy, T. E. (1980) A projection of species extinctions, in The Global 2000 Report to the President: Entering the 21st Century, pp. 323–31, Council on Environmental Quality and Department of State, Washington Government Office.

Marshall, J. (1992) Patterns of distribution of plant species in the fields and their margins, in: P. Greig-Smith, G. Frampton and T. Hardy (eds), *Pesticides, Cereal Farming and the Environment. The Boxworth Project*, HMSO.

Martin, P. S. (1984) Catastrophic extinctions and the late Pleistocene blitzkrieg, in: M. H. Nitecki (ed.)(1984) *Extinctions*, University of Chicago Press.

Morgan, R. P. C. (1986) *Soil Erosion and Conservation*, Longman Scientific and Technical.

Peet, R. (1969) The spatial expansion of commercial agriculture in the nineteenth century: a von Thunen explanation, *Economic Geography*, **45**, 283–301.

Pimentel, D. *et al.* (1995) Environmental and economic costs of soil erosion and conservation benefits, *Science*, **267**, 1117–23.

Potts, G. R. and Aebischer, N. J. (1994) Population dynamics of the Grey Partridge, *Perdix perdix* 1793–1993: monitoring, modelling and management, *IBIS*, **137**, S29–S37.

Smith, F. D. M., May, R. M., Pellew, R., Johnson, T. H. and Walter, K. (1993) Estimating extinction rates, *Nature*, **364**, 494–6.

Steadman, D. W. (1995) Prehistoric extinctions of Pacific Island birds: biodiversity meets zooarchaeology, *Science*, **267**, 1123–31.

Turner, B. L. II and Meyer, W. B. (1993) Environmental change: the human factor, in: M. J. McDonnell and S. T. A. Pickett (eds)(1993) *Humans as Components of Ecosystems*, Springer Verlag, 40–50.

United Nations Economic Commission for Europe (1991) UN, Geneva.

United Nations Environment Programme (1992) Article 2, *Biodiversity Convention*, p.27.

Vitousek, P. M., Ehrlich, P. R., Ehrlich, A. H. and Matson, P. A. (1986) Human appropriation of the products of photosynthesis, *BioScience*, **36**, 368–73

Wilson, E. O. (1988) *Biodiversity*, National Teaching Press, Washington.

Wilson, J., Evans, A., Grynderup Poulsen, J. and Evans, J. (1995) Wasteland or oasis? The use of set-aside by breeding and wintering birds, *British Wildlife*.

HUMANS AS ECOLOGICAL AGENTS

CHAPTER 2

Prepared for the Course Team by Dick Morris

2.1 Introduction

Chapter 1 suggested that humans have a major impact on species, communities, populations and ecosystems and that in many areas of the world, it may be difficult to find cases where there is no human impact on ecological processes. In this Section we are going to look at humans themselves, to see how and why they have such a major effect. A major aspect is the sheer size of the human population, but there are other factors. Commoner (1972) and Ehrlich and Ehrlich (1990) suggested that the extent of human impact is the product of **Population, Affluence** and **Technology** ($I = P \times A \times T$). An alternative formulation (Turner and Meyer, 1993) is that the important factors are **Population, Production** and **Consumption** ($I = P \times Pr \times C$). Population appears in both models, for obvious reasons, but what exactly is involved in the other suggested factors? Like all organisms, we need food to survive, but it is the way we obtain this food, and undertake other aspects of everyday life that produces our ecological impact.

❑ Based on the sorts of interactions that were considered in Book 1, list some of the ways in which you, as an individual, interact with other species, communities and ecosystems.

■ There are a number of ways. First, there are **feeding interactions**. We act directly or indirectly as a herbivore/predator on crops and exploited livestock.

Secondly, we directly modify the **conditions** affecting other species – the construction of the houses we live in profoundly affects the immediate ecosystem, and our living in them continues to do so, since most of us deliberately modify conditions in the house and any adjoining garden to suit chosen species.

Thirdly, we use various materials besides food which could be **resources** for other organisms, or our use of these materials affects the conditions for other organisms. Water is the most obvious example, and extracting raw materials, such as metals used in the manufacture of appliances, can have major effects on the conditions at sites of extraction.

Finally, we discharge various waste materials into the surroundings which can also affect conditions for other species. Household wastes are generally only a minor influence, but the combustion products from the fuel we use for transport and heating are a significant source of carbon dioxide and other biologically active materials. The provision of the goods and services that we purchase also results in discharge of wastes.

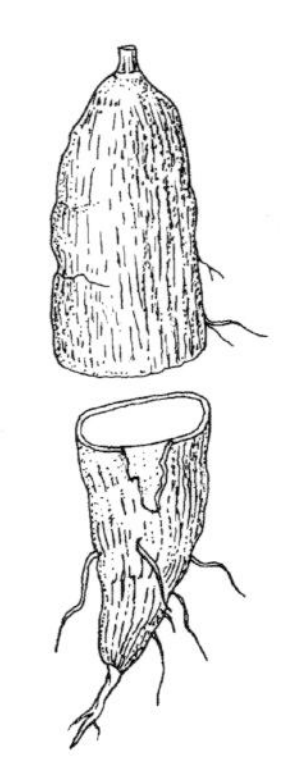

cassava root
Manioc esculenta
(× 0.125)

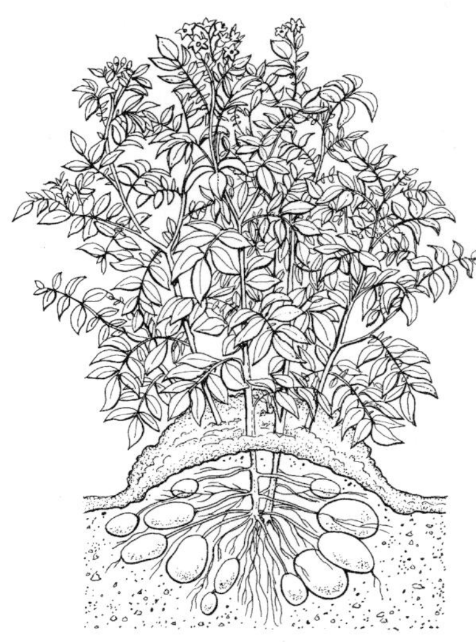

potato
Solanum tuberosum
(× 0.0625)

Amaranthus leucocarpus
(× 0.125)

The following Sections look at some of these effects in turn, and relate them to the 'multipliers' of the effects per human.

2.2 Feeding relationships of humans

Humans are omnivorous, and show few specialized feeding mechanisms.

❑ From general knowledge, identify the major items used as human food.

■ The major foodstuffs ('staples'), which supply both carbohydrates and protein, are derived from graminaceous plants, the cereals wheat, rice, maize, sorghum, millet and to a lesser extent oats, barley and rye. Less widely used carbohydrate staples are the starchy roots of cassava (*Manioc esculenta*) and potato (*Solanum tuberosum*), grain from amaranth (*Amaranthus leucocarpus*) and other fruits such as cooking bananas or plantain (*Musa* spp.). The protein supply from these staples is supplemented either by grain legumes, or by livestock products.

We have already looked briefly at some aspects of current methods of producing cereal staples, but it is useful to look back at some earlier aspects of human food seeking, to see how these have changed over time.

2.2.1 The origins of agriculture

The first recognizably human societies probably developed in Africa, and are believed to have been **hunter–gatherers** relying on the same food sources as other omnivores. Their diet might have included seeds, fruits, animal products such as eggs and honey and those animals that could be caught without too much expenditure of effort.

❑ From general knowledge, what would be the advantage of animals and animal products as food?

■ Animal tissues, and products such as eggs, have high protein content. The protein also has an **amino acid** composition close to the ideal for humans, so is of higher value than plant proteins.

Humans are **social** animals and, by operating as a group, are effective hunters, despite not having the physical adaptations of specialist carnivores. In addition to being social animals, we also have hands with opposed thumbs, and a form of intelligence which is associated with tool using and, more importantly, **toolmaking**. Hunter–gatherer societies presumably discovered that using sharp stones to crack open nuts or to separate meat from bone gave better access to food sources than was available to other generalist feeders. Kinaesthetic coordination of hand and eye in throwing stones or other found objects, and later spears, etc., increased the hunting efficiency of early human populations. Use of found products for skin cover and **shelter** would have expanded the potential climatic range available to these populations. Early humans also used **fire** to increase the digestibility (Book 4, Chapter 1) of foodstuffs through cooking, as an aid to hunting and for the deliberate manipulation of vegetation.

The few surviving examples of hunter–gatherer cultures have probably only persisted in areas where it is difficult or impossible to practise settled agriculture. This makes it difficult to estimate the population densities that could be sustained by hunting–gathering in more favourable environments. However, in at least three separate regions of the Northern Hemisphere, about 12 000 years ago, there developed more settled forms of society using fire and simple tools. Around such settlements, the ground would be disturbed either deliberately or haphazardly.

banana plant *Musa* spp.

❑ What are the likely characteristics of species that would establish on such disturbed ground?

■ The plants would be ruderals (Book 2, Chapter 4) with a large investment in seed.

By selective removal of plants with small seeds, and by saving and planting large seed from other species, early agriculturalists were able to obtain increasing amounts of food from a given area, and to create increasingly large settlements.

The three Northern Hemisphere centres where these developments appear to have begun are shown in Figure 2.1. They are, broadly:

(1) In the Middle East, an elliptical area currently comprising Israel, Syria, Jordan and the borderlands between Iran and Iraq.

(2) In Central America, an area to the south and east of Mexico City.

(3) In north-western China, between the north China plain and the western Chinese and Mongolian deserts.

Figure 2.1 Centres in the Northern Hemisphere where cereal-based agriculture probably first developed.

In all these three centres, the dominant food crops were grains: wheat, oats and barley in the Middle East, maize in Central America and millets in China. Common features of all these centres are their location in semi-arid areas (to which the grasses were particularly adapted), the presence either of readily worked stones for tool manufacture or of animals whose defensive horns were usable as tools, and high physiographic diversity. In the Middle East, where wild ancestors of sheep, cattle and goats were found, these species were also domesticated. Similar domestication of livestock seems not to have emerged in the other two centres. It has been suggested that the movement of a sophisticated hunting society across the Bering Straits into North America about 13 000 years ago resulted in the extinction of much of the large animal fauna in a wave spreading southwards (see Question 1.7). The presence of a diverse megafauna in the Americas prior to this date may have lessened the pressure for domestication of species and, after its extinction, the opportunities for domestication were reduced.

In the wet tropics, grain-based agriculture was climatically less appropriate, and the settled systems relied more on starchy tubers, such as cassava, yams, etc. These, along with a range of other perennial species, provided continuous vegetation cover which reduced the opportunities for loss of nutrients through leaching by rainfall.

Even at this early stage, humans were probably having a significant effect on the ecology of the areas that were inhabited. By the time that Columbus landed in 1492, much of America either supported, or had supported, large human populations operating relatively settled forms of agriculture. These included extremely complex forms in Central America and parts of what was to become the USA, such as the 'chinampa' system (Figure 2.2) practised in the flood plains of the closed valley of Mexico City. This consisted of a network of canals separating islands 3–10 m wide and up to 100 m long, constructed of mud scooped from the canals. Weed and sediment from the canals and human excrement was used each year to supply nutrients to the raised islands. A range of annual crops including maize, beans, peppers and grain amaranths was grown. Seedlings of some of the crops were grown on floating mats of vegetation in the canals, prior to being transplanted on to the islands.

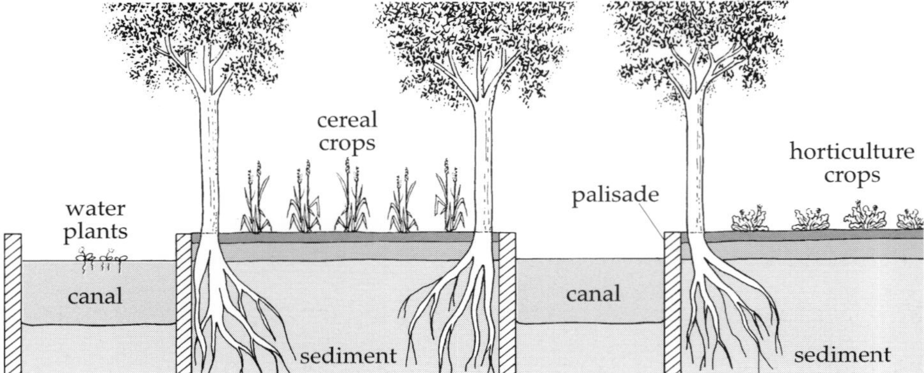

Figure 2.2 The 'chinampa' system of agriculture practised in Central America prior to European arrival.

Summary of Section 2.2

- Humans have food requirements that can be provided from a range of sources, which now include staple crops and animal products.
- Early human societies relied on hunting and gathering of food, but developed skills in the use of tools and in group operation which assisted in obtaining food resources.
- Settled agriculture developed in several areas, using different staple foods depending on the climate.

- The early forms of settled agricultural societies also domesticated various animal species.
- Settled forms of agriculture probably allowed higher population densities to be sustained than would be possible with hunter–gathering forms in comparable environments.
- Sophisticated forms of settled agriculture developed in areas such as Central America before European settlement.

Question 2.1 *(Objectives 2.2 & 2.3)*

Outline the major differences between the feeding interactions of humans and those of other animal species.

Question 2.2 *(Objective 2.2)*

Use the concepts of handling time, searching time (Book 2, Section 4.5.3), assimilation efficiency and production efficiency (Book 4, Chapter 1) to suggest reasons why human hunter–gatherer populations increased.

2.3 The importance of support energy

One of the biggest differences between human food production and the feeding mechanisms of other species is in energy relationships. In Book 4, we looked at the flows of energy through ecosystems, mainly mediated by the transfer of carbon compounds, with losses of energy to the environment at each transfer. In a hunter–gatherer society, a similar analysis could be applied, but the model does not fully describe the energy relationships of modern human society. In addition to using fire to cook food or to clear vegetation, early humans discovered how to use fire to work metals, and so moved from tools made of stone or bone, to metal ones. It does not need much imagination to recognize the increased efficiency of a human equipped with a bronze or, better still, an iron axe or hoe in modifying the vegetation community to provide for human needs.

This use of fire in the **manufacture** of products is only one example of human use of different forms of energy.

❑ List the five basic forms of energy.

■ (i) Potential; (ii) kinetic; (iii) thermal; (iv) chemical; and (v) radiant.

We can classify forms of energy in other ways. Energy derived from food which is involved in metabolism is termed **somatic energy** in contrast to that which is entirely external (**extra-somatic energy**). For most animals, energy relations only involve somatic energy. The only significant form of extra-somatic energy for most animals is **solar radiation**, used directly by ectotherms to raise their core body temperature (Book 1, Chapter 3). In a few cases, such as **cleaning symbioses** (Book 1, Chapter 1), animals may gain some non-nutritional advantage from energy expended by another species. In contrast, humans make extensive use of extra-somatic energy and our access to this is probably the dominant feature of our ecological interactions.

There are three major routes whereby early human societies obtained and used extra-somatic energy. **Fire**, the conversion of chemical into thermal energy, was probably first. **Domesticated animals** were used by humans to provide extra-somatic energy to assist in hunting and for **draught power** (pulling implements or loads), both of which increased the efficiency of the unaided human as a predator/herbivore. The third route involved the **kinetic energy of wind and water** for transport and to operate machinery. In all three cases, the original energy source was solar radiation, but the time-scales and mechanisms involved, and the rates of release of energy (i.e. the rates of working that can be obtained) differ widely.

This leads to the distinction between **ambient** (i.e. current) and **fossil** forms of energy. The kinetic energy of wind and water is derived directly from ambient solar energy. For domesticated animals, food energy is derived from current or recent solar energy via photosynthesis. Most combustible materials were recent or current biomass, but humans also used **fossil fuels** such as coal, oil and natural gas, formed from biomass from an earlier geological era. We now also use radioactive materials as fossil fuels. Ambient energy forms are sometimes referred to as **renewable**, and fossil forms as **non-renewable** sources.

❑ Recall from Book 1 a potential problem associated with our use of fossil fuels.

■ It is claimed that the burning of fossil fuels is a major contribution to increasing the concentration of carbon dioxide in the atmosphere, which may cause climatic changes through global warming.

Using the different forms of extra-somatic energy enables humans to make enormous changes to their interactions with other organisms and the environment. The energy flows involved are quite complex, and the most effective way to explain them is by using audiovision.

You will need the audiocassette and the AC Notes for 'Energy flow in managed ecosystems' to work through this Section. The cassette points out the major features of the energy flow diagrams in the Notes. For each system, you will summarize the energy flows in a standardized manner, and calculate various ratios of energy flows.

This energy analysis explores the relationship between the **flows** of energy through a managed ecosystem and the expenditure of energy by humans, often as kinetic energy, in *regulating* those energy flows. This is summarized in Figure 2.3 – human expenditure of kinetic energy is used to turn the 'taps' that regulate some of the flows of energy within the ecosystem. Study Figure 2.3 carefully. It is important to understand that although expenditure of kinetic energy is shown influencing the flow of food energy to the human consumer, this kinetic energy does *not* pass directly to the human as part of the food.

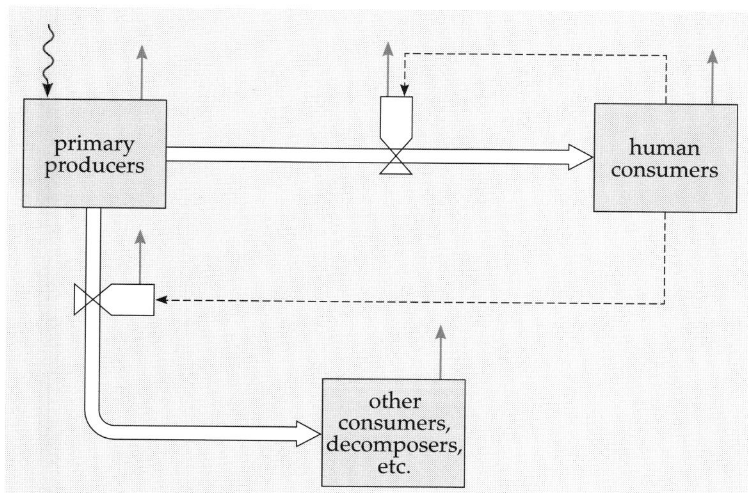

Figure 2.3 The major flows of different forms of energy in a human-dominated ecosystem.

To use a real example, you might expend about 0.5 MJ (an hour's hard work) over a season, digging, weeding, etc., a square metre of soil planted to potatoes, to obtain, on average, a crop with a food energy content of 10 MJ. The 0.5 MJ of energy expended is entirely dissipated as kinetic and heat energy and does not re-enter the food chain. Humans also use other forms of energy to regulate their food chains, and it is important not to confuse the different forms and flow paths of energy. In the audiocassette 'Energy flow in managed ecosystems', we look at four examples of agricultural systems, and try to evaluate the flows of energy (shown in Figure 2.3) from published data. The four systems are (i) a pre-industrial society in Papua New Guinea, (ii) a historical example of semi-industrial agriculture from 19th-century Britain, (iii) a recent, if somewhat unusual, British farm and (iv) recent US grain maize production – see Figures 2.4–2.7. The data for these systems are presented as Tables and Figures in the accompanying Notes in the *Companion for Book 5*.

Turn to the AC Notes, and play the audiocassette now.

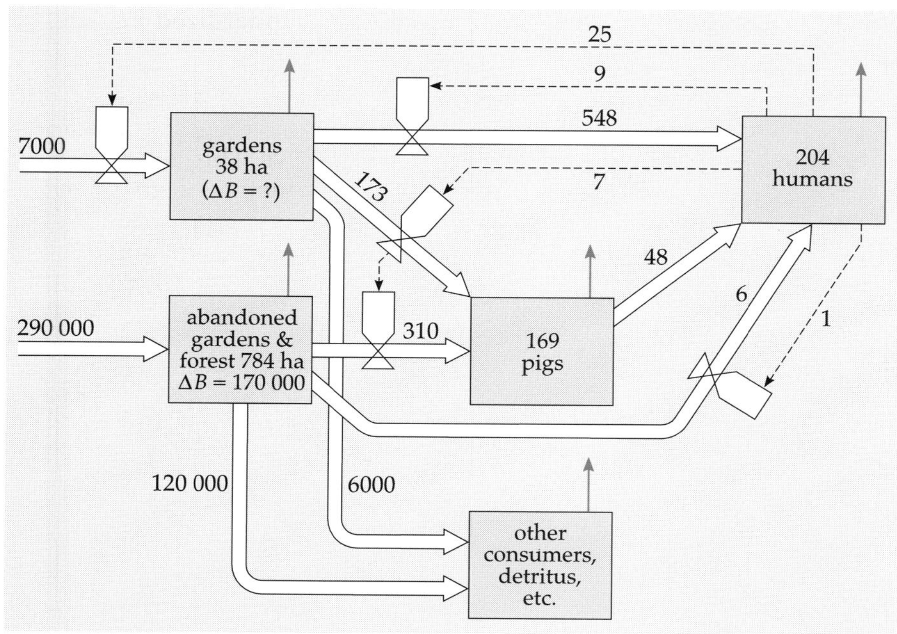

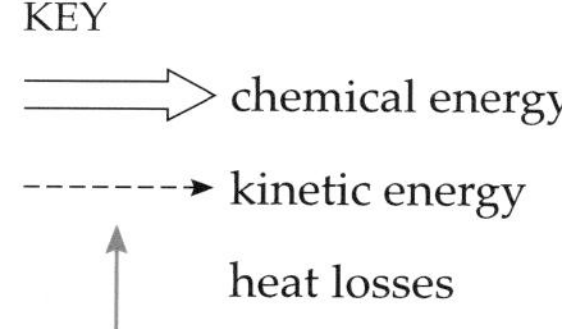

Figure 2.4 Energy flows through the Tsembaga Maring ecosystem, Papua New Guinea in the 1960s. Values are given as GJ.

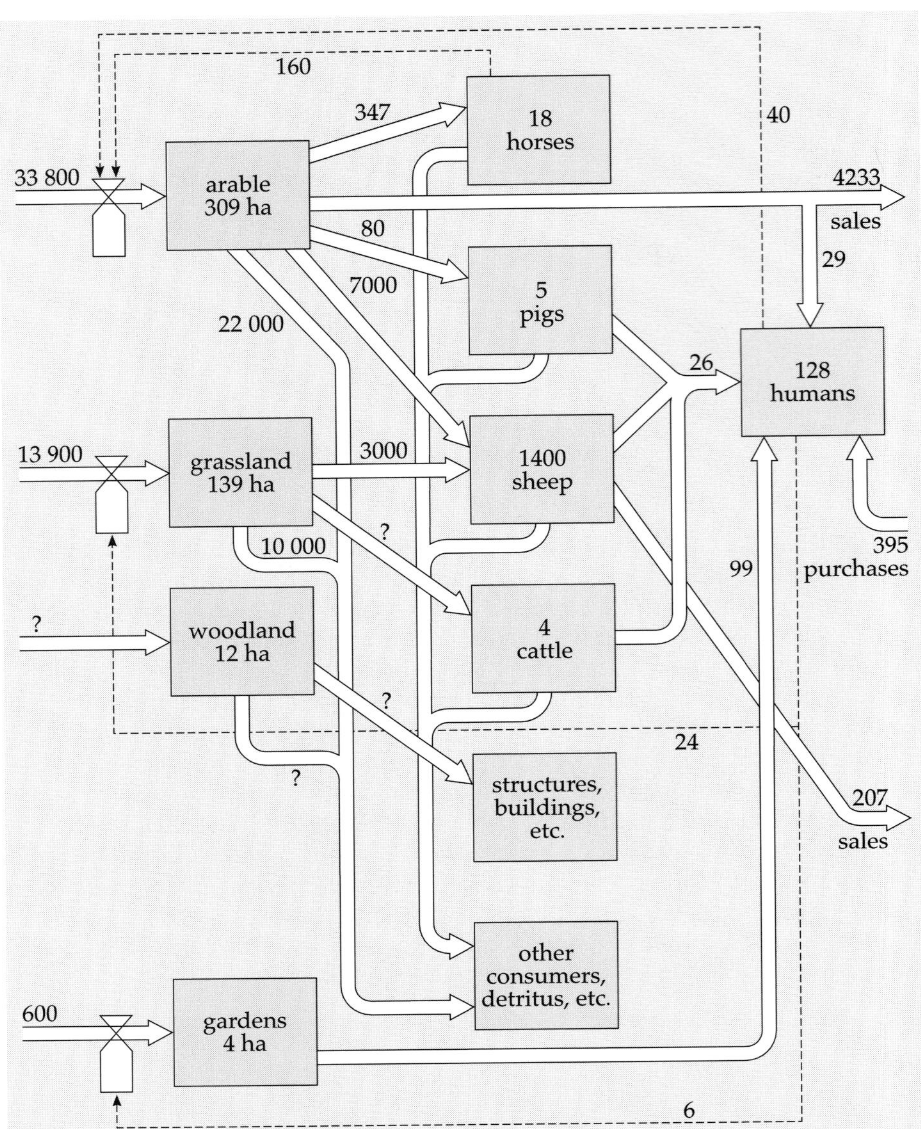

Figure 2.5 Energy flows for Fyfield Manor, 1820. Values are given as GJ.

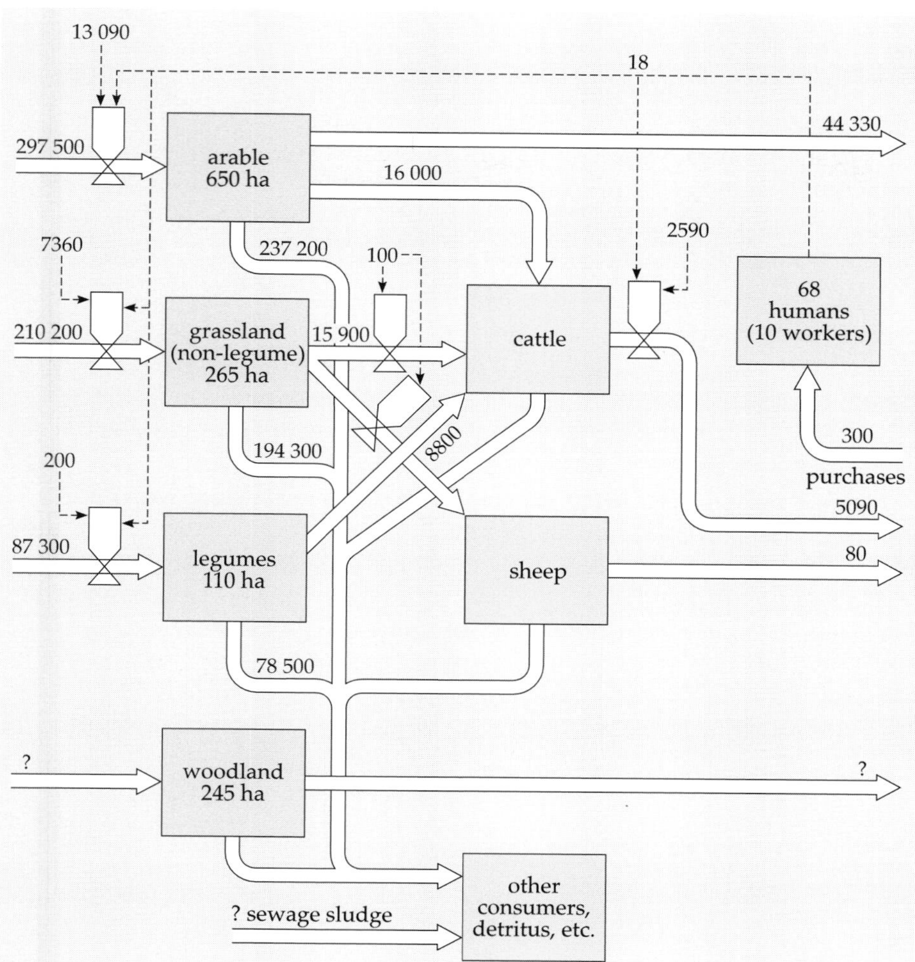

KEY

chemical energy

kinetic energy

Figure 2.6 Energy flows for a Wiltshire farm, 1983. Values are given as GJ.

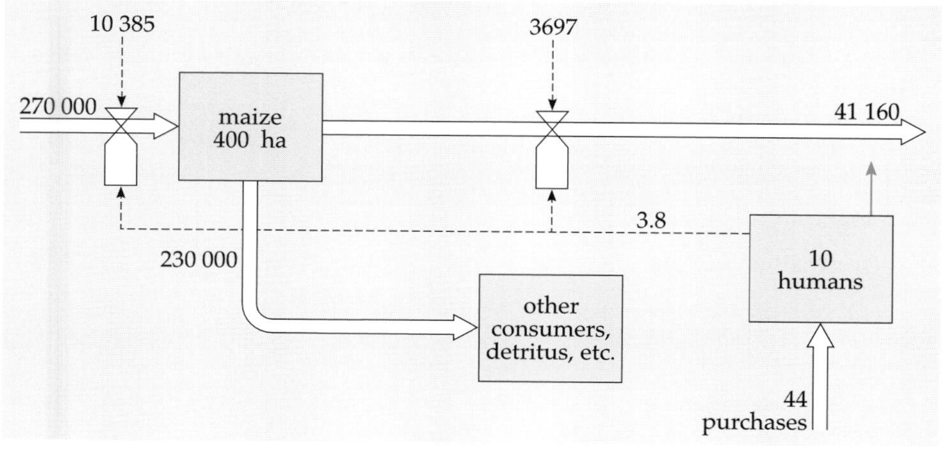

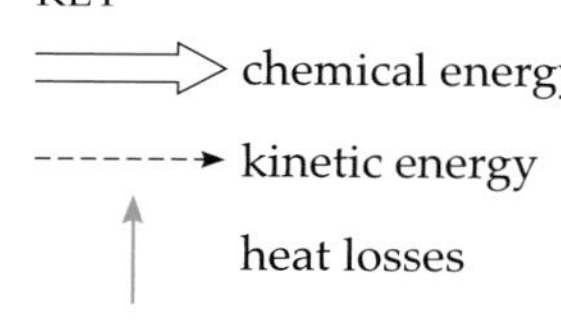

Figure 2.7 Energy flows for US maize production, 1980. Values are given as GJ.

Summary of Section 2.3

- Humans differ from other animal species in their use of extra-somatic energy.
- This energy comes from a range of ambient or fossil sources. These include:
  - (i) current or recent biomass, used either directly as a fuel, or indirectly via draught animals;
  - (ii) kinetic energy of wind and water;
  - (iii) fossil fuels.
- Use of this extra-somatic energy in agriculture has been particularly important in increasing the amounts of food energy obtained per hectare, through the use of draught animal power and through the industrial synthesis of fertilizers.
- Current agricultural methods use a very large amount of fossil fuel energy, but the amount used per hectare is several orders of magnitude less than the solar input.
- The general use of fossil fuels may be causing changes in atmospheric carbon dioxide concentration, which may affect climate.

Question 2.3 *(Objective 2.1)*

Distinguish between somatic and extra-somatic energy, and between ambient and fossil sources of energy as used by humans.

Question 2.4 *(Objective 2.4 & 2.5)*

(a) Table 2.1 provides a summary of the energy analysis data studied on the audiocassette. For each of the systems considered, fill in the blanks in the Table.

(b) Which of the four systems in Table 2.1 provides the greatest amount of food energy in relation to the total expenditure (human work and fossil fuel energy) in regulating the food production process?

Table 2.1 Some comparative aspects of the energy flows in four different systems. Values are given as GJ ha^{-1}.

	Tsembaga	Fyfield	Wiltshire	US maize
average net primary production		107	580	675
food energy produced for humans	0.73		48.30	102.90
food energy consumed by humans within the system		1.18	0.24	0.11
human work expended on food production	0.050	0.150	0.014	
support energy used in food production	0.0		18.7	35.2

Question 2.5 *(Objectives 2.4 & 2.5)*

To what extent does human effort in producing crops represent recycling of energy through the food chain?

Question 2.6 *(Objective 2.5)*

Why, despite the lower use of fertilizers on the Wiltshire farm, is support energy use per unit of food produced approximately the same for US maize and the Wiltshire farm examples?

Question 2.7 *(Objective 2.5)*

You can assume that the average rate of input of solar energy in the US maize growing area throughout the year is 400 watts m^{-2}, over a 12-hour day. What are the relative magnitudes of the total amount of solar energy received, and support energy used, per hectare per annum in this area?

2.4 Materials and the environment: pollution and resource depletion

The preceding analysis has concentrated on extra-somatic energy use in food production, but much of the energy we use is for the **chemical processing of materials**. Fossil fuels have enabled large-scale synthesis of a wide range of materials, including **metals**, **ceramics** and **plastics** and other **organic chemicals**. Many in the last group are biologically active, the so-called **effect chemicals**, which have amplified human effort in modifying ecological processes.

❑ Give some examples of effect chemicals which you commonly use.

■ Pesticides and synthesized fertilizers are two examples.

An early example of industrial chemistry was the manufacture of the **alkali** sodium carbonate, which can be reacted with fats to form **soap**. This involved the **Leblanc process**, which was introduced in the 1820s from France to St Helens in Lancashire, where the basic ingredients of salt, limestone and coal were readily available. In the Leblanc process, common salt was mixed with sulphuric acid in a shallow open pan, stirred and gently heated to produce sodium hydrogen sulphate and hydrogen chloride. The sodium hydrogen sulphate and residual salt were then roasted on a furnace to produce a yellowish solid 'salt cake' (sodium sulphate) and more hydrogen chloride. The chemistry is:

$$NaCl + H_2SO_4 \rightarrow NaHSO_4 + HCl$$

$$NaCl + NaHSO_4 \rightarrow Na_2SO_4 + HCl$$

❑ What would happen to the hydrogen chloride from this process?

■ Hydrogen chloride is a gas so it would escape into the air, as would sulphur oxides and dust from the fuel used to roast the salt cake.

The salt cake was broken into lumps, mixed with its own weight of limestone ($CaCO_3$) and half its weight of coal and coke and fired in a rotating furnace. The sulphate was reduced to sulphide, which then reacted with the calcium carbonate:

$$Na_2SO_4 + 2C \rightarrow Na_2S + 2CO_2$$

$$Na_2S + CaCO_3 \rightarrow Na_2CO_3 + CaS$$

After a period, the molten mass was run into iron trucks where it solidified into a porous grey substance called 'black ash'. Sodium carbonate is soluble in water whereas calcium sulphide is not, so by repeatedly washing the black ash, the desired **soda ash** could be leached out of the mixture and separated from the insoluble alkaline waste, called 'galligu'.

The solution of soda ash was purified and the product once more roasted to give the commercial soda ash.

❑ Identify the main energy source for this process. Was this an ambient or fossil source?

■ The energy source used was coal, which is a fossil source.

❑ Identify some of the important inputs and outputs associated with this process which would have ecological effects.

■ The inputs to the process were salt, limestone, coal and sulphuric acid. Mining of the first three would directly disrupt the areas concerned. Outputs from the process included hydrochloric acid gas, sulphur oxides, dust and the galligu. The gases and dusts discharged to the air would be likely to affect organisms directly, and the galligu tips covered significant areas.

By the mid-19th century, the alkali industry had grown considerably and discharged many tons of hydrogen chloride into the air every day. *The Times* for 12 May 1862 described the effect of the emissions:

> 'Whole tracts of country, once as fertile as the fields of Devonshire, have been swept by deadly blight till they are as barren as the shores of the Dead Sea'.

Hydrogen chloride is soluble in water and could have been washed from the waste gases, but there was no legal or commercial incentive to do this. Eventually, after a campaign by Lord Derby, whose estate was affected by these emissions, the Alkali Act of 1863 was passed, requiring that 95% of the hydrogen chloride should be removed from gases escaping from the chimneys of alkali works. The Act represented the first and for about 100 years, the only, **air pollution emission standard** and also introduced an Inspectorate with powers to enter factories to protect the atmosphere and prevent damage to property by acid gases. Subsequent Alkali Acts widened the scope of the Alkali Inspectorate's powers and it is still operational, although now as part of the wider Environment Agency in the UK.

All manufacturing involves using energy to **extract** and **process physical resources** from the environment, to produce artefacts for human use. During production and use of an artefact, **waste products** and **waste heat** may be returned to the environment (Figure 2.8). Table 1.18 showed that world rates of extraction or production of some materials were of a similar order to natural material movements. It is difficult to give average figures for the amounts of energy used and waste material created per tonne of product but, as an indication, some data for copper extraction are given in Table 2.2.

Table 2.2 Energy and waste production associated with the extraction of copper.

Process	Energy use/ MJ t^{-1} processed	Waste produced
mining	120	100 t rock t $copper^{-1}$
crushing and froth flotation	280	1000 t rock t $copper^{-1}$
smelting and converting	28 400	sulphur dioxide
fire refining	4140	ND*
electrolytic refining	2950	ND

*ND = no data.

❑ Oil provides approximately 40 MJ l^{-1}. How much oil would be needed to provide the energy for smelting a tonne of copper ore?

■ From Table 2.2, it requires 28 400 MJ, equivalent to over 700 litres of oil, approximately half a tonne.

Some of the waste products may be inert, such as quarry wastes, and their ecological effects are limited to obscuring existing habitats (and, in the process, creating new ones). Others, like the acidic fumes from the Leblanc process, have more widespread and damaging effects. Where a waste material *causes damage to people, or to their property*, it is then defined as a **pollutant**, but it is important to note the human-centredness of this definition.

❑ Suggest a situation in which waste heat from a process could be a pollutant.

■ One example is the discharge of warm water from an industrial process into a watercourse. This could affect the community of organisms present there. But note that, legally, this would only be defined as pollution if some or all of the affected organisms were someone's property.

Industrial activity can therefore change both the availability of **resources** for other species and the **conditions** in which they live (Book 1, Chapter 3). Ecologically, much of the concern about human activity has been centred on changes in conditions as a result of pollutants that we generate, but the supply of resources could also be a problem, both for humans and for other organisms. Technologically, **material resources** include water, for which we could be in competition with other organisms, and also specialized items such as metallurgical minerals and fossil energy sources. More recently, the technological definition of resources has been broadened to include 'the environment', in recognition that this is often used as a **sink** for the disposal of waste materials. Since the early 1970s, there has been concern that some or all of these resources could 'run out', with serious effects for human society, and possibly for other organisms.

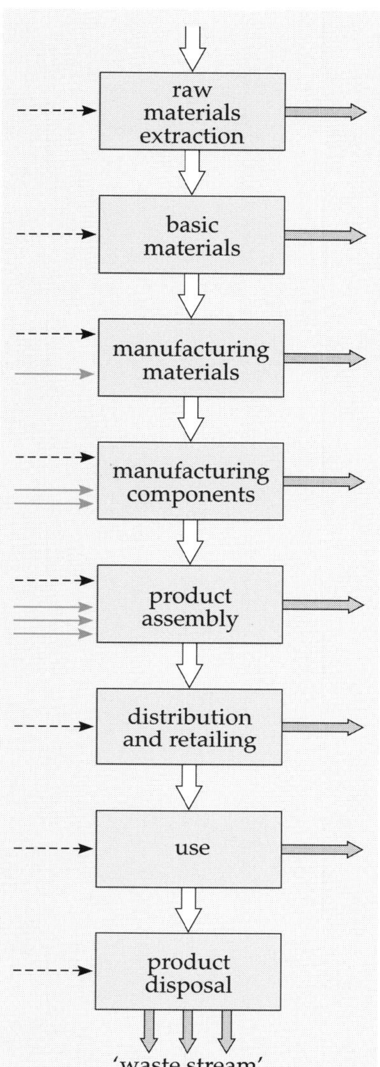

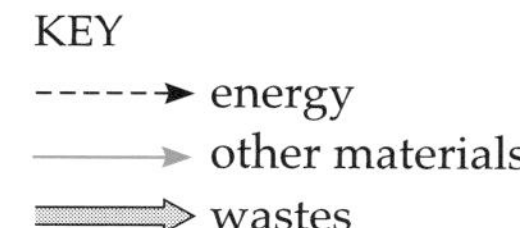

Figure 2.8 The production system associated with human artefacts.

An important aspect of the technological definition of resources is the concept of **reserves** and **usable reserves**. The total amount of a material resource in the world does not change, but the form in which it exists affects its usefulness. Globally, aluminium is the third most abundant element, but most of this is in the form of clay minerals from which the metallic element we use cannot currently be extracted. The only naturally occurring form of aluminium which is currently usable is the oxide, **bauxite**, from which metal can be extracted by a very energy-intensive process (about 250 MJ per kg of aluminium). Bauxite is found as **ore deposits** in various parts of the world, mixed with other materials. The amount of bauxite present per tonne of material in a deposit varies and this affects the cost of extraction, as does the technology available at the time. For any mineral resource, there is a lower limit to the **concentration** of ore in a deposit that it is economically worthwhile to extract. Only that proportion of the global resource that exists in deposits with a concentration greater than this threshold can be considered to be a reserve. The usable reserve (that which would actually be worth extracting with current technology, energy costs and metal price) is even less.

The extent of a usable reserve therefore depends on the **price** that can be obtained for the resource. Conventional economic theory says that if a material is in short supply, its price will rise. This argument has been used to suggest that there is no need to be concerned about depletion of resources, since when a material becomes scarce, its price will rise and this will increase the amount of the reserve that is usable. Table 2.3 shows the changes in the world reserves of copper and zinc from the 1940s to the early 1990s as estimated by the US Bureau of Mines. They define reserves to include both those deposits which are currently economically viable and those which 'can reasonably be expected to become economically viable'. The data cannot therefore be regarded as absolute, but do indicate the way reserves can apparently increase over time while the resource is being used.

Table 2.3 World reserves of copper and zinc as estimated by the US Bureau of Mines. Values are in 10^6 t (data from Hodges, 1995).

Period	Copper	Zinc
1940s	91	54–70
1950s	124	77–86
1960s	280	106
1970s	543	240
1980s	566	296
1993	590	330

If the rate at which reserves become usable is insufficient to achieve an acceptable price, then alternative processes may be developed, using different resources. One other change in the use of resources is the increase in **recycling**. In 1995, 40% of aluminium, 45% of copper and 70% of lead consumed in the USA was from recycled material. For the first time, the overall consumption of metals in the USA from recycled sources exceeded consumption of newly mined material.

The description of material processing indicates some of the reasoning behind the models of human impact given at the beginning of this Chapter.

❑ Explain how the multipliers of production and consumption included in one model relate to material processing.

■ The model assumes that each unit of artefacts produced or materials consumed has an impact on ecological processes, either through pollution resulting from extraction, processing and use (see Figure 2.8) or through depletion of some resource. As production and consumption increase, so impact will increase proportionately.

The alternative formulation where impact was defined as the product of population, affluence and technology makes similar assumptions. As affluence increases, more products are demanded by consumers so the amount of materials processed, and the effects that this incurs, also increases. Technology affects the amounts of resources, energy and wastes involved per unit in supplying the products. In the equation, technology appears as a simple multiplier and there is an implication that as the 'level of technology' rises, so the impact of humans on the biosphere also increases. Indeed, Ehrlich (1994) specifically suggested that human use of support energy could be used to predict rates of extinction of other species. His predictions assumed that global energy usage rates would continue to grow at the historical rate of 2.3% y^{-1} that had occurred from 1970 to 1990. However, this negative view of technology may not be entirely fair. Technologies usually change so as to become more efficient, in the sense of using less resource (and possibly creating less waste material) per unit of product. Ehrlich (1994) did note that UK energy consumption, which had grown by 40% between 1925 and 1955, grew by only 3% between 1955 and 1975. Between 1972 and 1993, it hardly changed at all.

❑ What evidence has been given that technology can change to decrease the impact per unit of human activity?

■ The data for the increased recycling of metals in the USA indicate that fewer new mineral deposits need to be worked to supply metals. This could reduce the impact of mining, although the total impact of recycling would need to be assessed carefully. Similarly, the Boxworth and Northern Irish data for cereal production showed that some pesticide inputs can be reduced without major effect on yield (Section 1.2).

We will return to the assessment and management of human impact on the environment in the next Chapter.

Summary of Section 2.4

- A major aspect of human activity is industrial production of materials and artefacts, using inputs of materials and fuels, producing both desired and undesired (pollutant) outputs.
- The requirements for resources and outputs of undesired emissions can affect other organisms, by restricting the availability of resources for them, or changing the conditions in their environment.
- The models of the total impact of humans summarize these effects using the variables of affluence and technology or production and consumption as multipliers of population.
- Some early chemical processes produced copious pollutant outputs, which led to legislation being introduced to control emissions. This legislative control has continued to the present day.

- More recent manufacturing processes may use less energy and fewer materials and produce fewer undesired emissions per unit of output.
- The economic factors that determine the level of reserves of material resources mean that it is difficult to say when a particular resource might be exhausted.

Question 2.8 *(Objective 2.5)*

For a typical day of your life, identify the major demands for materials and fossil fuel energy that you make, and potentially polluting wastes that your activities produce.

Question 2.9 *(Objective 2.7)*

In 1950, world consumption of copper (excluding consumption in the Soviet Union and China) was 2787×10^3 t. In 1991, worldwide consumption was $10\,714 \times 10^3$ t. Using the data given in Table 2.3, what would be the estimated time to exhaustion of reserves on these two dates? Suggest one factor which may extend the life of reserves.

2.5 Biological resources: extinctions and genetic engineering

The recognition that 'the environment' is also a resource in the technological sense potentially gives economic support to public concerns over pollution, loss of habitats, ecosystems and, particularly, loss of species. Humans rely on other species for a number of products as well as food, and if, as suggested in Section 1.4, we are causing an increased rate of species extinction, we need to consider the factors which may make species vulnerable to extinction. Humans have long used selective breeding to affect the **genetic material** that is available and we now have the technology of **genetic engineering** which enables us to do the same across species barriers and, potentially, to create new species.

2.5.1 Mechanisms of extinction

In Book 3, there was a discussion of the problem of rarity. This is interesting in itself, but it also has implications for the likelihood of extinctions. Small populations are more likely to be extinguished by catastrophes, or to suffer decline because of excessive inbreeding. For a species to become rare in a given area, the balance between the basic population processes of births, deaths and migration must be such that numbers decline. **Hunting** directly affects mortality and possibly birth rate, and hunting by the Polynesian people who reached New Zealand around AD 1000 is claimed to have resulted in the extinction of 11 species of the large flightless herbivorous birds called moas. Humans can also affect species by **habitat destruction**, but there are some specific features of populations which make them particularly vulnerable. Lawton (1994) has identified a number of features of populations which are relevant, and Thomas and Morris (1994) reviewed the situation with respect to British invertebrates, for which some of the best data regarding extinctions are available. Lawton noted that there is a general correlation between a species' **geographic range** and its **population abundance**. That is, species with a wide geographic range also tend to occur in dense populations, although there are numerous exceptions. The reasons for this are not fully understood, but one possibility is that species with a very broad niche are able both to exploit resources over a wide geographic range and, on a more local scale, to achieve high densities of population. Metapopulation models (Book 3), which include the effects of migration between populations, also predict that species which occupy a high proportion of the possible sites will also have high densities within these sites. The converse of this is that species with a narrow niche are also likely to occur at low densities, and so suffer double jeopardy. A second relevant observation is that the range occupied by species in a given taxon is smaller near the equator, and increases towards the poles.

❑ What are the implications of these two observations for the susceptibility of species to extinction?

■ They suggest that the probability of extinction is greater in tropical than in temperate areas.

Given these general observations, the destruction of tropical rainforests could well result in the loss of a disproportionate number of species.

Within the UK, Welch (1993) examined the information about invertebrate species noted in the *British Red Data Book of Insects* as being presumed extinct or vulnerable to extinction, in relation to the land cover classes (Section 1.6) in which they were found. The results are shown in Figure 2.9.

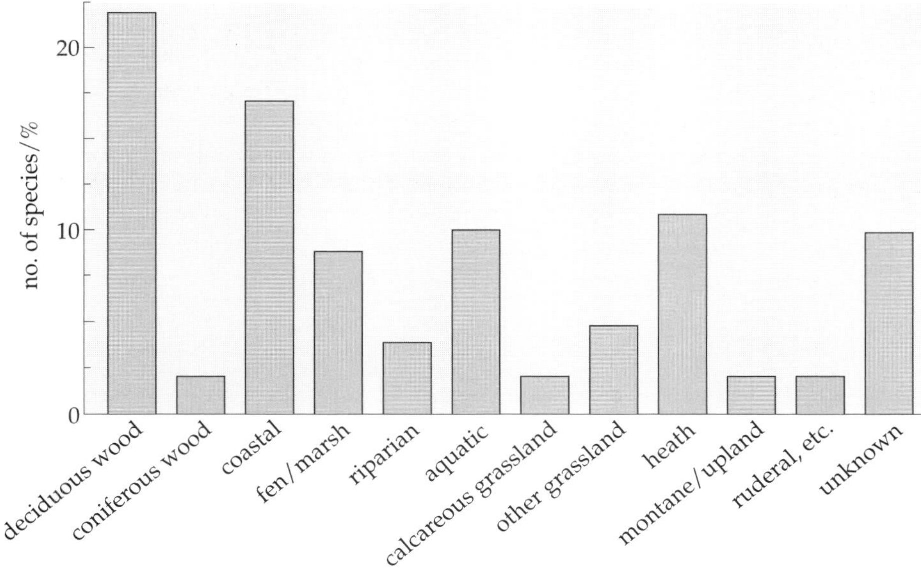

Figure 2.9 The percentage distribution of *Red Data Book* invertebrate species presumed extinct or vulnerable to extinction in 12 principal types of land cover classes.

Thomas and Morris (1994) distinguished between two changes which might occur in the different land cover classes leading their invertebrate species to become endangered. In some cases, the area occupied by that class may have been severely reduced, as in the conversion of lowland grassland (and calcareous grassland in particular) to arable. In total, the area of semi-natural grassland in England and Wales had decreased from 5.8 million ha in 1932 to 0.2 million ha in 1984. The area of heathland has also declined greatly; 86% of the approximately 40 000 ha of heathland in Dorset in the 18th century had gone by 1990. In other cases, changes in human activity may have allowed succession to take place within the land cover class, leading to loss of particular habitats within these.

❑ Over the past 100 years or so, the major losses of land cover classes in the UK have affected grassland, heath and fen/marsh. Do the data in Figure 2.9 suggest that loss of these classes has been a major factor in pushing species towards extinction?

■ Not clearly. Although heath and fen/marsh classes contain above-average numbers of threatened species, calcareous grassland has one of the lowest numbers. The actual area of deciduous woodlands has not changed nearly so much over this period, but these show the highest numbers of threatened invertebrate species.

To investigate the effects of successional stage on endangered species, Thomas and Morris categorized the habitats of threatened species according to their seral stage (Book 3, Chapter 3) as in Figure 2.10.

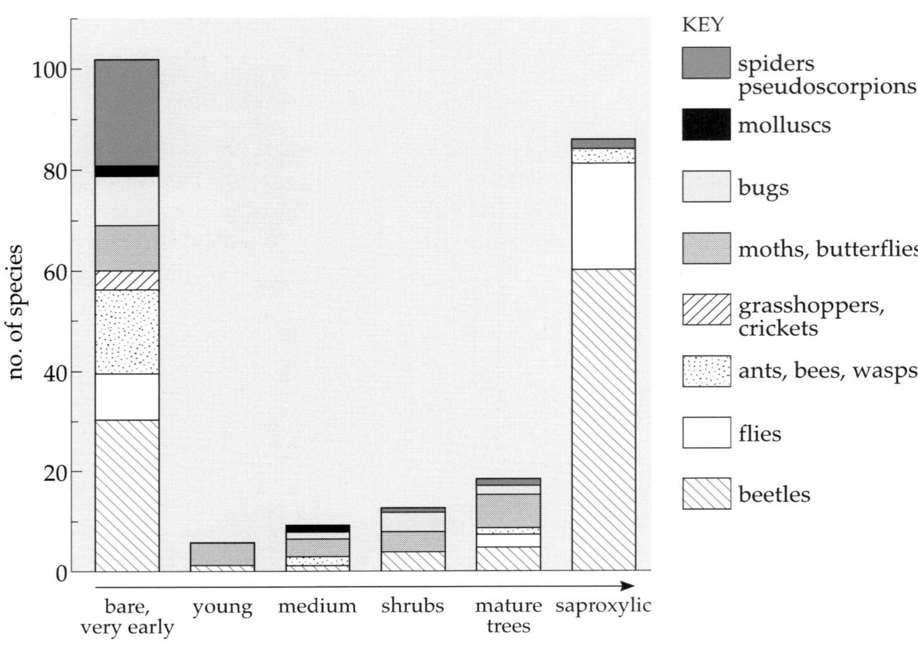

Figure 2.10 The seral stages inhabited by *Red Data Book* invertebrate species presumed extinct or vulnerable to extinction in woods, grasslands, heaths and dunes.

Figure 2.10 suggests that endangered species are strongly associated with very early seral stages of succession, or they are **saproxylic**, that is, found in dead wood, typical of late successional stages of woodland in the UK. This second class might be expected, since the area of **ancient woodland** in the UK has been reduced (Book 3, Chapter 1) much more than has the total area of woodland. The association with bare ground or very early succession seems odd at first, because arable agriculture aims precisely to create a very early successional stage, and as we saw earlier, occupies a major proportion of the land surface. The explanation suggested for this anomaly is that temperature is a critical factor. While arable areas briefly contain areas of bare ground, these are rapidly vegetated with dense, tall crops, reducing the amount of solar radiation reaching the soil and hence reducing soil temperatures. In both cases, the endangered species probably have very narrow niches (in the case of saproxylic species, in terms of food source, for the species of early successional stages, in terms of temperature tolerance) which tallies with Lawton's suggestion that species with narrow niches are particularly at risk.

Land use change is possibly the major way in which humans increase the chances of extinction for susceptible species. Historically, another important mechanism has been the introduction of alien species into fragile ecosystems. A major cause of the losses of island species mentioned earlier was the accidental introduction of rats and the deliberate introduction of other predators such as cats to islands where there were no comparable predators present. Although regulations regarding transport and introduction of alien species are now strict in most countries, the increasing volume of international travel increases the opportunities for alien introductions.

2.5.2 Genetic manipulation

Since the earliest form of settled agriculture developed, humans have exerted selective pressure on other organisms, although the changes arising from this were slow and little different from the results of other pressures. Since the early 1970s, humans have developed methods to manipulate directly the genetic composition of species and this may have profound implications.

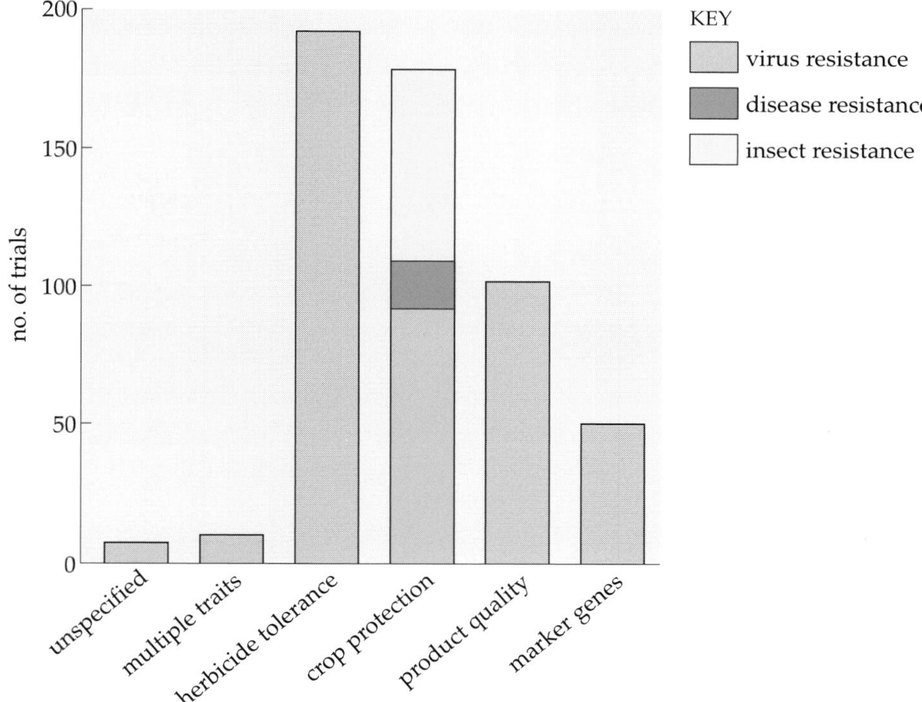

Figure 2.11 Approved field trials of transgenic plants involving different traits.

Genetic engineering usually involves the selection of specific pieces of genetic material (DNA) from one source and their insertion into the genetic material of another organism. Crop plants are a major target of genetic engineering. Figure 2.11 shows the distribution of traits which were being sought in trials worldwide in 1992, involving more than 30 species into which genes from another species had been inserted, creating **transgenic** plants. Most of the work involved four major crops: (i) tobacco *Nicotiana tabacum*; (ii) tomatoes *Lycopersicon esculentum*; (iii) potatoes *Solanum tuberosum*; and (iv) oilseed rape *Brassica napus*. Maize *Zea mays* and cotton *Gossypium hirsutum* were also the subject of trials, but work on the other major cereal staples was much less advanced.

- ❑ Which trait was the subject of the greatest number of trials in 1992?

- ■ Herbicide tolerance: using crops tolerant to an otherwise non-selective herbicide enables growers to use this to achieve high levels of weed control. Recall from Chapter 1 the importance attached to weed control in cereals.

The potential ecological effects of these transgenic species are a matter of intense debate. It is possible that a genetically engineered organism could compete more successfully than the species from which it was derived, and so replace that species in the field. In outcrossing species, hybrids between the transgenic species and unmodified ones could also change competitive relations in communities. Since most of the species where transgenic individuals have been created are crops, which are **obligate cultigens**, i.e. dependent on humans for their survival, this may not be a problem, but we will return to this topic in Chapter 3.

Summary of Section 2.5

- Ecosystems, communities and some individual species may be regarded as an important resource.
- The extinction of species would reduce the amount of this resource that is available.
- Species which are susceptible to extinction appear to be those associated with early successional stages, or those with a particularly narrow niche.
- Although humans often create early successional habitats, these do not necessarily exhibit the characteristics necessary for the survival of threatened species, and such habitat change may have been the cause of some extinctions.
- Introduction of alien species to island communities may be associated with major changes in the populations of indigenous species.
- Genetic engineering enables us to transfer genetic material between species, introducing new genotypes.
- These new genotypes may have ecological effects if introduced into the field, but the extent of any problems is currently difficult to predict.

Question 2.10 *(Objective 2.9)*

Section 1.2 described the decline in numbers of those birds classified as farmland species. Is this decline in numbers in accordance with the data presented by Thomas and Morris for susceptibility to extinction among invertebrates?

Question 2.11 *(Objective 2.10)*

Plant breeders have inserted a gene into oilseed rape plants which enables the plant to break down glufosinate, a widely used, non-selective herbicide. Plants germinating from seed spilled during harvest may become weeds in succeeding crops. In an experiment to compare the finite rate of increase (λ) of normal (control) and genetically engineered (known as Basta) rape lines, seed were sown in three years into cultivated or uncultivated land. The values of λ are shown in Figure 2.12.

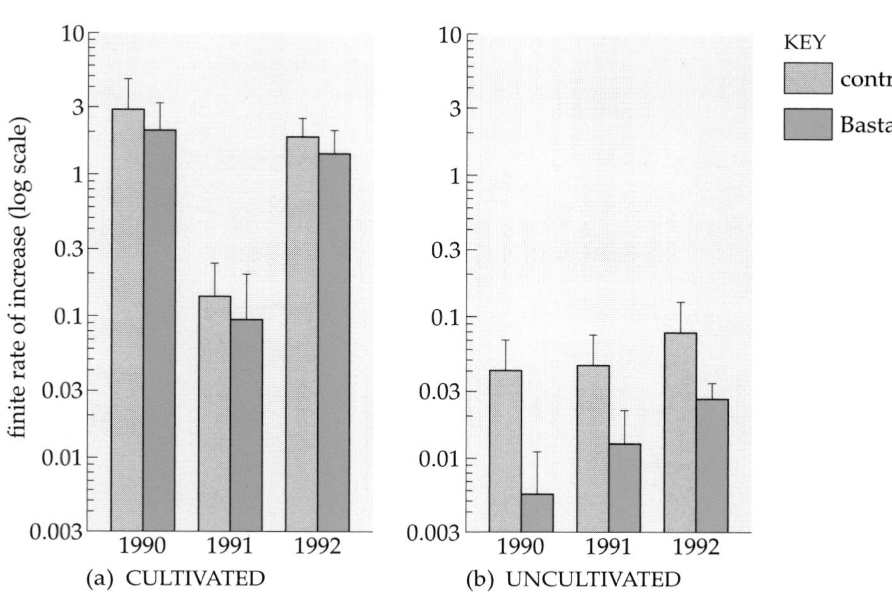

Figure 2.12 The finite rate of increase for two genetic lines (control and Basta) of oilseed rape in three harvest years, when sown into (a) cultivated or (b) uncultivated ground.

(a) Describe the results of the experiment.

(b) What value of λ would have to be exceeded for one of the lines to expand its population between years?

(c) Does the experiment suggest that genetically engineered rape could become a weed in succeeding crops?

2.6 Human population growth

In both the models suggested at the beginning of this Chapter for estimating human effects on ecosystems, population was regarded as a simple multiplier applied to some other variables representing the nature of human activity. Figure 2.13 overleaf shows two different models of the estimated change in numbers of the world's human population over a period of 10 000 years. In the first case (Figure 2.13a), population is assumed to increase exponentially, and is plotted using a linear scale. The second (Figure 2.13b) assumes that population growth is better modelled by a series of hyperbolic curves, and is plotted using a logarithmic scale. Clearly, the implications for potential effects of humans on the environment are very different for the two models. In Book 2, the possibility of continued exponential growth was dismissed as being unrealistic for most species, which tend to approach, or cycle round, some sort of plateau in numbers reflecting the carrying capacity of their environment and their relationships with other species. This suggests that the second model of human populations, with each period of growth leading to a plateau, would be more typical. According to this model, after human populations had tended to stabilize at each level, some change must have occurred which allowed a further increase to some new 'carrying capacity'. The separate waves could be associated with successive phases of human cultural evolution. So the first wave might represent the first recognizable humans, which reached a population limited by the food obtainable from hunting and gathering. Making of basic stone or bone tools increased the efficiency of hunting and also allowed some cultivation of crops in settled agricultural communities. These agricultural communities reached limits dictated by each new phase of toolmaking and its associated food production methods. The most recent are the industrial communities, where improvements in food production, sanitation and possibly in health care allowed a further period of expansion.

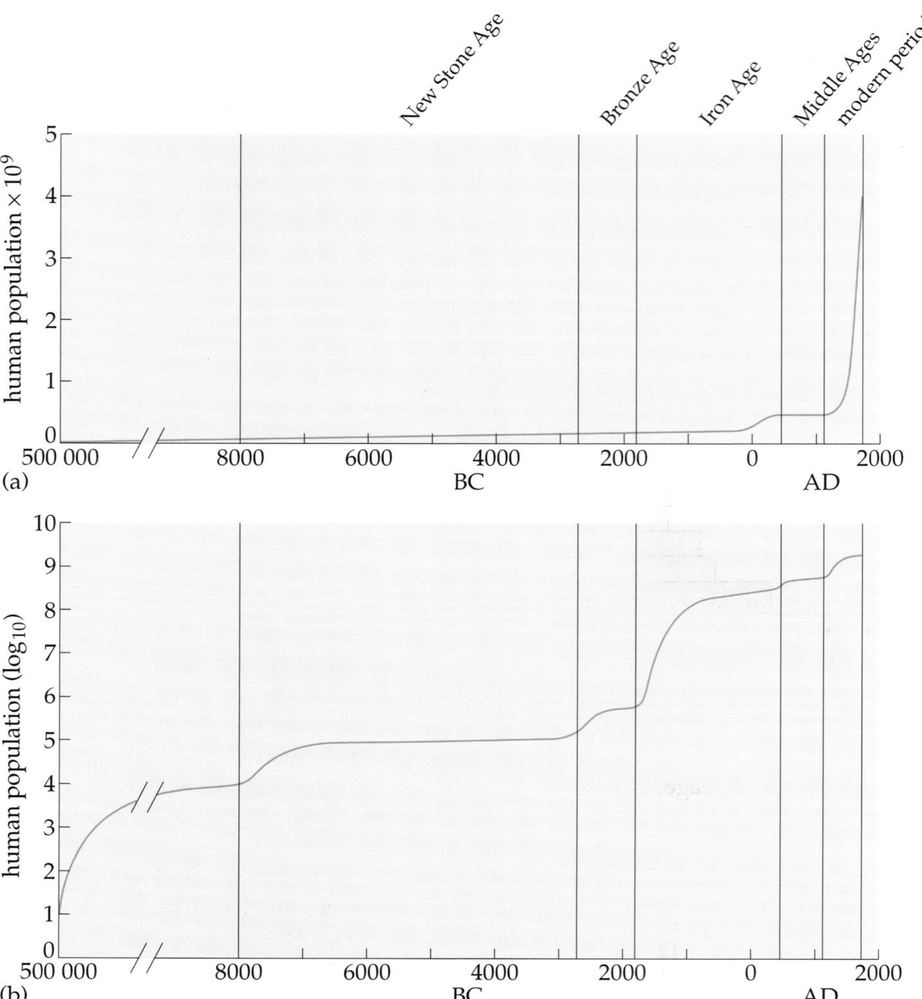

Figure 2.13 Two possible versions of the growth of human populations over the period since the species became distinct, plotted on (a) linear and (b) logarithmic scales.

The long-term data for human population numbers are insufficiently precise to give any real indication as to which of these two models is more appropriate, so we need to look at some of the current data on human populations to see if these give any indication of the way change is likely to occur.

❑ What type of life history (Book 2, Chapter 5) does the human species exhibit, and what other species would you expect to exhibit a similar life history?

- The human life cycle exhibits continuous iteroparity; individuals breed at all times of the year, and can breed repeatedly. Many mammals breed repeatedly, but relatively few show the almost total absence of seasonality of humans. This is usually a characteristic of species of non-seasonal environments.

The age structure of human populations should be comparable to that of other long-lived mammals in a stable environment. Figure 2.14 shows the age structure of the population of red deer *Cervus elephas* on the Scottish island of Rhum in 1957, and similar data for the human populations of Malawi in 1979 and the UK in 1981.

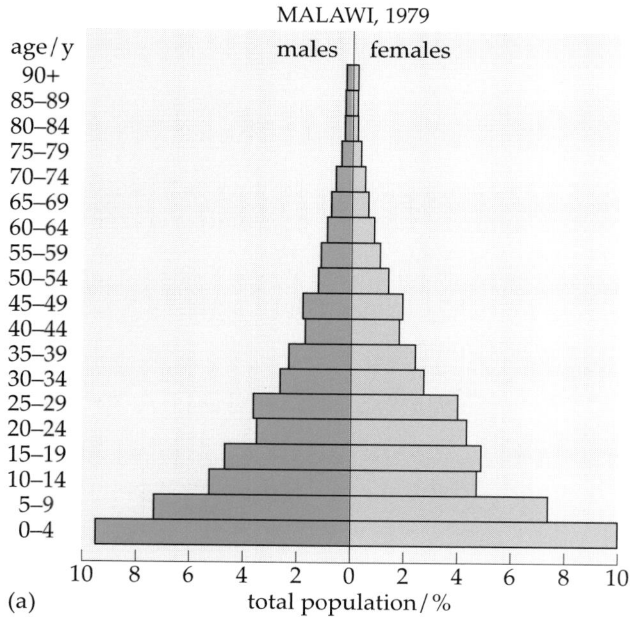

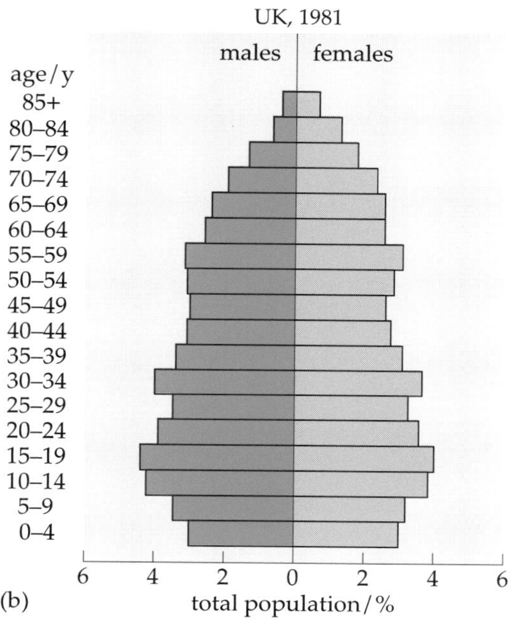

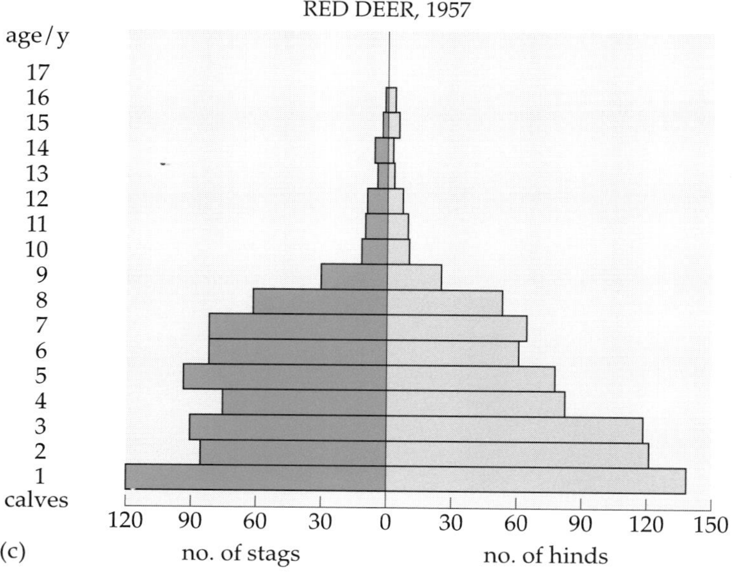

Figure 2.14 Age structure of populations: humans in (a) Malawi and (b) UK, and (c) red deer.

❑ What features distinguish these three population structures?

■ The graphs of population age structure for humans in Malawi and the red deer have a similar general shape, with steadily declining numbers in the older age categories. In contrast, the structure for UK shows a much less pyramidal shape, with relatively constant numbers in the first 20 age classes up to about 60 years.

Although Book 2, Chapter 1, showed that it can be misleading to impute birth and death rates from a static life table such as Figure 2.14, the pattern of mortality of the UK population is likely to be different from that of Malawi, which is closer to that of a 'natural' population. What the figures do not show is the change in birth and death rates that have occurred and are possibly occurring in different human societies.

❑ Mammals differ in their **fecundity**. List five major aspects of reproductive performance which can vary to affect overall fecundity.

■ (i) Litter size; (ii) length of time between births; (iii) age at onset of reproduction; (iv) duration of reproductive life of females; (v) the proportion of adult females that breed.

❑ List three factors that determine what proportion of mammalian offspring survive to reproductive maturity.

■ (i) Predation; (ii) disease; (iii) food supply.

❑ Which of the factors listed in answer to the two previous questions would you consider to be unimportant in regulating *human* population size?

■ Litter size (i.e. number of offspring resulting from a single pregnancy) is probably unimportant, the proportion of births producing twins or greater numbers being relatively constant throughout the world at about 16%. Predation is unimportant, and the proportion of adult females that breed may not be a major factor.

❑ What factors are most likely to determine death rates for a human population?

■ Apart from war and accidents, death in humans almost invariably results either from disease, exacerbated perhaps by poor nutrition, or from 'old age'.

❑ (a) What resources affect the fecundity of mammalian populations in general?

(b) Which of these factors would also affect fecundity in human populations?

■ (a) Availability of food and territories.

(b) Availability of food could well affect human fecundity. The effective availability of territory may also be important, although it is determined more by social or economic norms than by absolute physical or biological limits.

Thus, the factors which could regulate human populations are the length of time between births, age at onset of reproduction and duration of reproductive life of females, disease and the availability of food and territory.

❑ Could any or all of these factors exhibit density dependence?

■ Availability of food is potentially density dependent, as is disease incidence. Age at onset of reproduction, duration of reproductive life and length of time between births are potentially dependent on the nutritional state of the female, so these could also be density dependent if food supply is limited.

Those who study human population dynamics are generally agreed that all these factors affect human population numbers. Despite this, there is a great divergence of opinion about the future state of the world population. The **population explosion**, as it is called, and its possible consequences, is a topic of endless debate.

One major distinction between human population regulation and that of other mammals is that human fecundity is, at least in part, the result of conscious decisions, rather than a simple physiological response to external biotic factors. Voluntary use of contraceptive techniques and abortion affects human fecundity and has few obvious analogies among non-human populations, although under unfavourable conditions other mammals may reabsorb fetuses. Humans can decide that the interval between births should be shorter or longer, not just because of current conditions but in anticipation of what conditions may be like in the future. The large families of the upper middle class in Victorian England were in part a physiological response to improved standards of nutrition, but also resulted from the recognition that contemporary rates of infant and childhood mortality would reduce the number of offspring surviving to maturity. This was amplified by the social norm that equated large well-fed families with prestige.

Despite these complications, we might expect human birth and death rates to be related to population density in comparable environments. Table 2.4 gives data for density of population and percentage net rates of change for a range of countries.

Table 2.4 Population density for a range of countries in 1990, derived from UN population data.

Region/country	Population density/ persons km^{-2}	rate of change/% y^{-1}
Africa:		
Angola	8	0.8
Egypt	56	2.3
Gambia	92	4.0
Ghana	69	3.0
Niger	7	2.6
Sudan	11	2.9
Zimbabwe	27	4.5
North America:		
Canada	3	2.6
Guatemala	92	2.9
Mexico	47	1.9
USA	28	1.1
South America:		
Argentina	12	1.2
Brazil	18	1.6
Colombia	30	1.7
Asia		
Bangladesh	800	2.1
China	125	1.2
India	274	2.9
Hong Kong	5506	1.2
Europe:		
France	104	0.4
Germany*	246	-1.1
Greece	78	0.7
UK	238	0.4
Oceania:		
Australia	2	1.1

*Data for former West Germany only.

❑ From Table 2.4 and your general knowledge, does it appear that availability of food has an important effect on human fecundity?

■ It may have an effect, but in the Table high net rates of increase occur in very different societies (e.g. Canada and Sudan).

This apparent anomaly forms part of the theory of the **demographic transition** (see Figure 2.15), which is based on observations of population trends in Europe from the 18th to the 20th century.

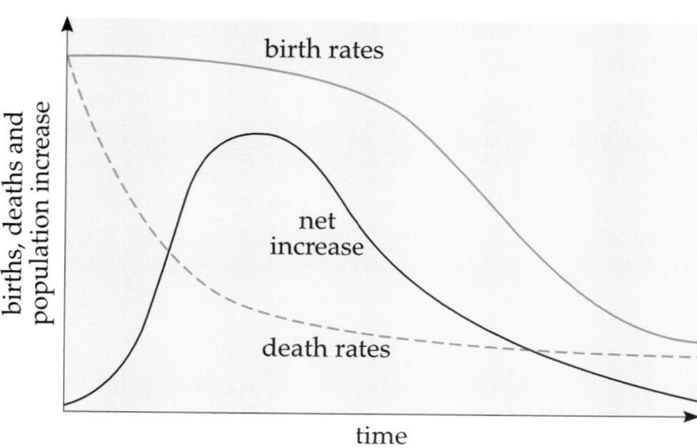

Figure 2.15 Changes in birth and death rates and in net rate of increase where a population exhibits a demographic transition.

In Europe during the 19th century, improvements occurred in access to food through improved technology of food production, but more importantly, through improvements in transportation making available grain supplies from America. There were also developments in understanding of **disease transmission** and in the technology of **sanitation**, leading to improvements in public health which resulted directly in a decrease in the death rate. Birth rates remained at their original level, or may even have increased due to improved medical care. The immediate result was a rapid increase in population, as in Figure 2.15. After a delay, however, birth rates fell to a lower level so that today birth and death rates in Europe are among the lowest in the world. In societies with high mortality, large numbers of children are an insurance for the future. Once a society recognizes that mortality rates have fallen, then the response is to reduce birth rates, by a greater proportion, so that the net rate of population increase declines, or may even become negative. This phased change from high birth/high death rates to low rates, in association with technical advances, is the demographic transition.

This model fits European experience well. What is not so clear is to what extent the same phenomenon is occurring or will occur, in those parts of Africa, Asia and Latin America that currently have high birth and death rates. Look back to Table 2.4 and try to decide whether it provides evidence for or against this general model.

The availability of food and resources for the world population is crucial to the occurrence of the demographic transition, and is itself crucially dependent on the transition occurring. Thus, there are two possible arguments:

(i) *if* sufficient food and other resources can be made available to all the world so that mortality is reduced, *then* birth rates will reduce and populations will ultimately stabilize;
or
(ii) *unless* birth rates are reduced, so that populations cease to grow rapidly, *then* not enough food and resources will be available at some time in the future.

Projections of the possible changes in human population have been made for various plausible estimates of future birth, death and migration rates. One set of these is shown in Figure 2.16. The 'central' projection, that is using the median values for the variables of mortality, fertility and migration, shows a considerable increase in the population of the 'less developed' countries, but possibly a decline in the population of the 'more developed' countries after the middle of the 21st century. If, indeed, population is a simple multiplier for the ecological effects of human activity, then these are likely to increase, unless we can find ways of reducing the effect per person. And therein lies a paradox. One of the underlying reasons for the demographic transition to lower rates of population increase is believed to be improvements in '**standard of living**'. These improvements result in increased infant survival and general life expectancy, which encourage humans to reduce the numbers of children born. However, higher standards of living have historically been associated with increased consumption of resources per person, and this consumption of resources may increase the ecological effects per person. In the following Chapter, we will examine some of the ways of managing human interactions with the environment.

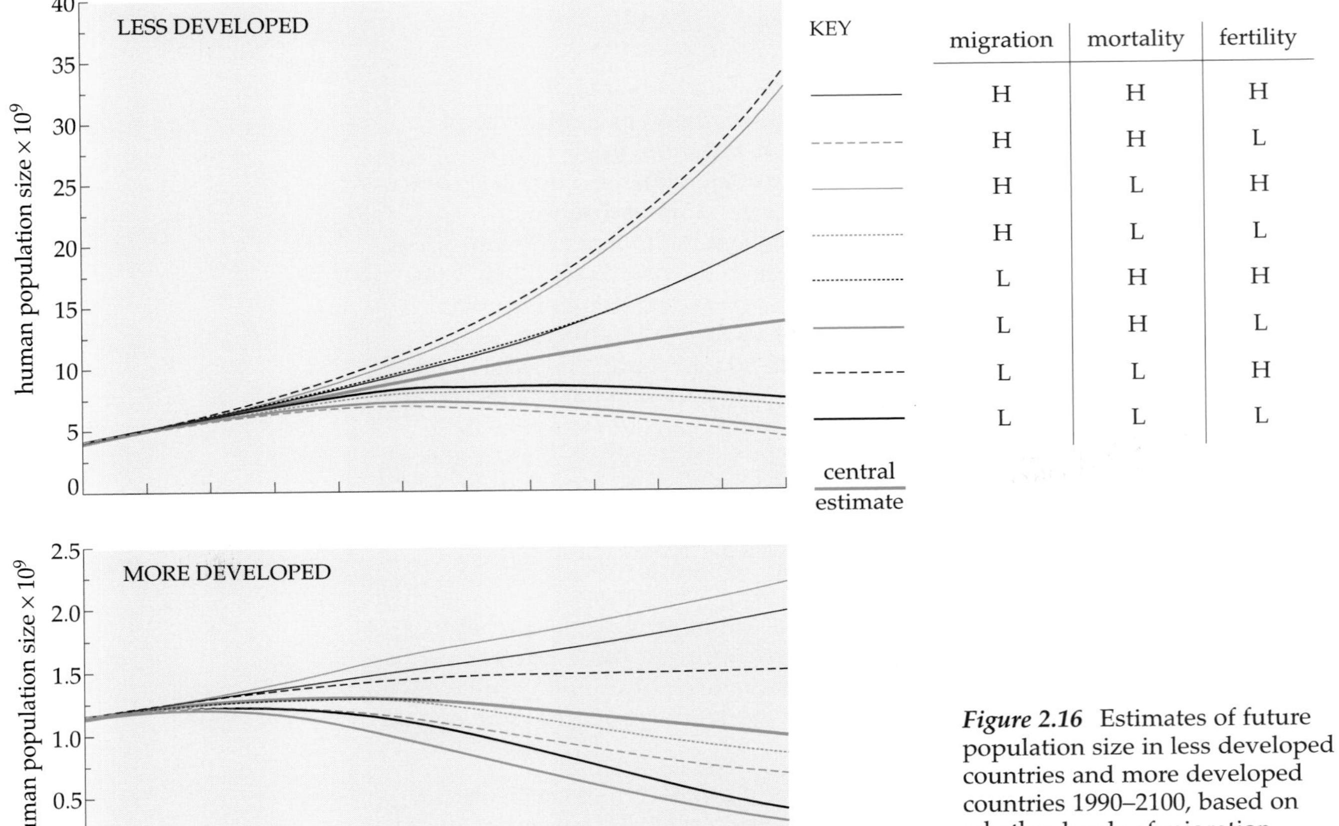

migration	mortality	fertility
H	H	H
H	H	L
H	L	H
H	L	L
L	H	H
L	H	L
L	L	H
L	L	L

Figure 2.16 Estimates of future population size in less developed countries and more developed countries 1990–2100, based on whether levels of migration, mortality and fertility are high (H) or low (L).

Summary of Section 2.6

- Human populations have been represented as increasing exponentially since the species was first distinct, or as increasing in a series of waves, with periods of stability between periods of more rapid growth.
- Human population age structures vary widely between different societies.
- The birth rate of human populations appears to be affected by the expected death rate, according to the theory of demographic transition.
- Death rates in human populations are affected by the technology and the standard of living available to that population.
- The future course of human population numbers, and of resource use, is uncertain.

Question 2.12 *(Objective 2.11)*

Figure 2.17 shows the age distribution for humans in China and Southern Asia (India and adjacent countries) in 1990, and a projected distribution for 2030. The projected distribution assumes the central estimate rates of population increase shown in Figure 2.16. Comment on the features of these life tables and on their implications for those countries.

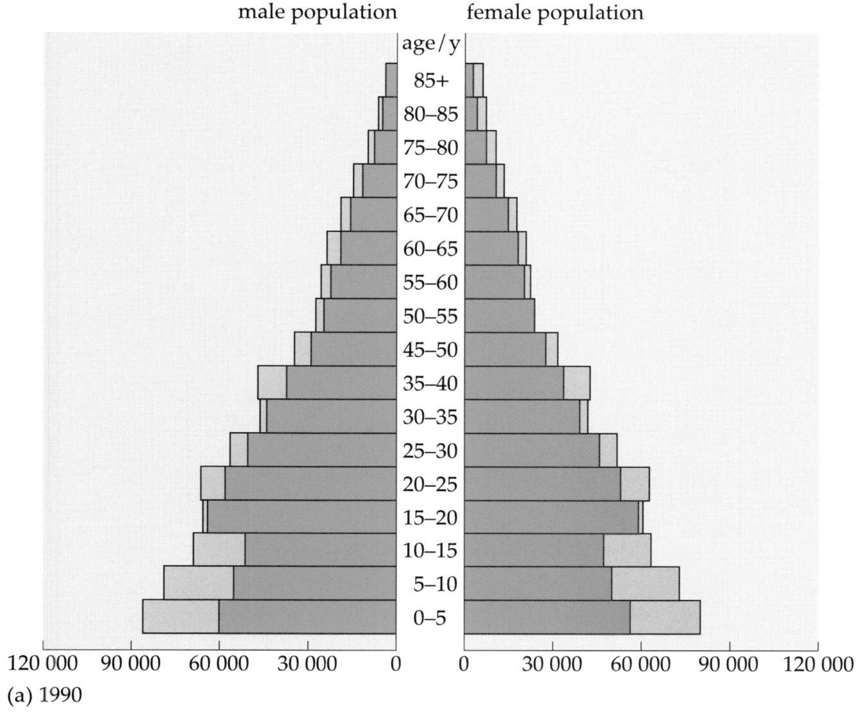

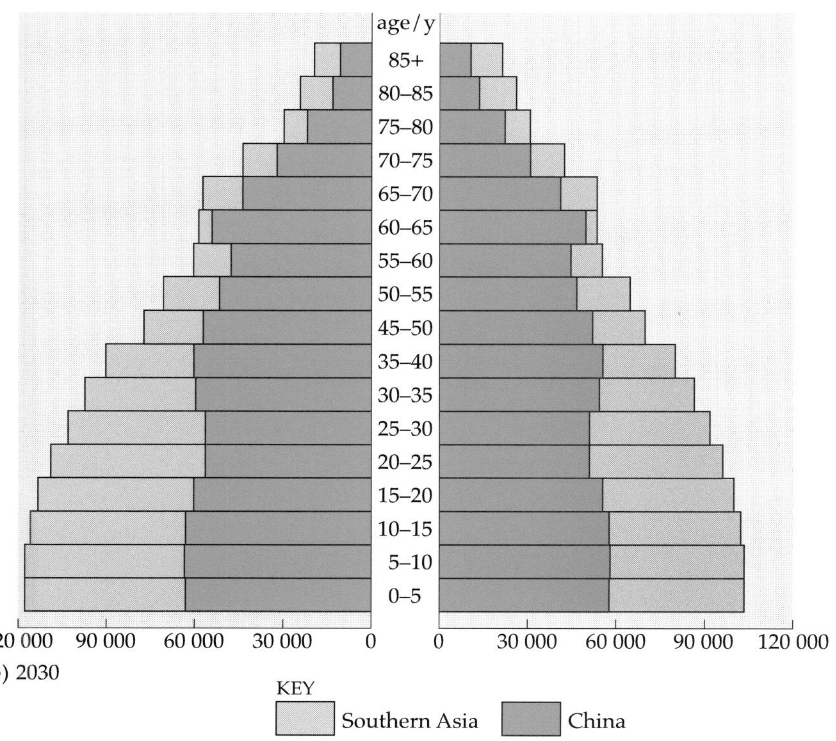

Figure 2.17 Age distribution of the human populations in China and Southern Asia in 1990 and a projected distribution for the same areas for 2030 on the assumption of central estimate growth rates.

Question 2.13 *(Objective 2.12)*

In 1970–75, the number of births per woman in Kenya was approximately 8, and this fell to 5.5 in 1988–93. In the early 1960s, 200 out of every 1000 children died before the age of two, and this decreased to around 62 per 1000 in 1994. Are these data in accordance with the theory of demographic transition?

Objectives for Chapter 2

After completing Chapter 2, you should be able to:

2.1 Recall and use in their correct context the terms shown in **bold** in the text. (*Question 2.3*)

2.2 Use the concepts learnt earlier in the Course to explain the growth in human populations from an early stage. (*Question 2.1 & 2.2*)

2.3 Describe the basic pattern of changes in methods of obtaining food during the evolution of human society. (*Questions 2.1 & 2.2*)

2.4 Distinguish between different forms of energy, and explain how use of support energy contributes to human activities. (*Questions 2.4 & 2.5*)

2.5 Given suitable data, conduct an analysis of the use of support energy in different food-producing systems. (*Questions 2.4, 2.5, 2.6, 2.7 & 2.8*)

2.6 Outline the ways in which human industrial activity may affect other species. (*Question 2.10*)

2.7 Recognize the importance of changes in technology in altering the ways in which humans affect other species. (*Question 2.9*)

2.8 Comment critically on predictions of the exhaustion of resources for human activity. (*Question 2.9*)

2.9 Recognize the ways in which human activity can lead to extinction of species and the factors which lead particular species to be vulnerable to extinction. (*Question 2.10*)

2.10 Identify some hazards arising from the use of genetically modified organisms in the field and comment on the extent to which these might occur. (*Question 2.11*)

2.11 Comment on the different possible future trajectories for human population numbers in relation to technological change and the demographic transition. (*Question 2.12*)

2.12 Given suitable data, identify situations where a demographic transition has occurred. (*Question 2.13*)

References for Chapter 2

Commoner, B. (1972) *The Closing Circle*, Knopf.

Ehrlich, P. R. (1994) Energy use and biodiversity loss, *Philosophical Transactions of the Royal Society, London B*, **344**, 99–104.

Ehrlich, P. R. and Ehrlich, A. H. (1990) *The Population Explosion*, Simon and Schuster.

Hodges, C. A. (1995) Mineral resources, environmental issues and land use, *Science*, **268**, 1305–11.

Lawton, J. H. (1994) Population dynamic principles, *Philosophical Transactions of the Royal Society, London B*, **344**, 61–8.

Thomas, J. A. and Morris, M. G. (1994) Patterns, mechanisms and rates of extinction among invertebrates in the United Kingdom, *Philosophical Transactions of the Royal Society, London B*, **344**, 47–54.

Turner, B. L. II and Meyer, W. B. (1993) Environmental change: the human factor, in *Humans as Components of Ecosystems* (eds M. J. McDonnell and S. T. A. Pickett), Springer Verlag, 40–50.

Welch, R. C. (1993) *An Assessment of the Invertebrates Associated with the Institute of Terrestrial Ecology's Land Cover Classes*, ITE.

ECOLOGY AND DECISION-MAKING

CHAPTER 3

Prepared for the Course Team by Dick Morris

The technological capabilities of humans and our large population size mean that we can produce large effects on other species and communities. However, for the same reasons we should also be able to manage these interactions in a rational way. Agriculture represents one directed application of the principles of ecology – the favouring of a small number of chosen species. In Chapter 3, we are going to look at some other examples of **environmental management**, where human activity is intended to achieve some desired balance between production of commodities for human consumption and the performance of populations and communities of other organisms. This is a rapidly growing field of activity, meriting its own professional institutions, and provides an interesting contrast to the somewhat jaundiced view expressed in the quote from Holdgate in the Introduction to this Book.

3.1 Environmental impact: analysis, assessment, management

'Environment and pollution' has become an increasingly important element of public concern in recent years in the UK and has been an issue for even longer in the USA and elsewhere. **Environmental impact analysis** (EIA) legislation was first introduced in the USA in 1969 with the National Environmental Policy Act (NEPA) and a European Community Directive in 1988 encouraged the adoption of EIA as a process in member states. Despite claims that UK planning legislation already covered these issues, several hundred Environmental Impact Statements were being made per year in the UK by the early 1990s and current UK legislation requires **Environmental Assessment** (notice the loss of the politically sensitive phrase Impact Analysis) of major developments.

There are several definitions of the requirements and process of Environmental Impact Analysis.

> 'to identify and predict the impact on the *environment* and on man's (*sic*) *health and wellbeing* of *legislative proposals, policies, programmes, projects and operational procedures*, and to interpret and communicate information about the impacts.'
> (Munn, 1979, italics added.)

> '… a technique and a process by which information about the environmental effects of a project is collected, both by the developer and from other sources, and taken into account by the planning authority in forming their judgements on whether the development should go ahead.'
> (UK Department of Environment, 1989.)

> … an assessment of the impact of a planned activity on the environment.'
> (UN Economic Commission for Europe, 1991.)

In some countries, EIA is mandatory, in others purely discretionary, and the activities subject to EIA and the extent of public participation also vary. The original NEPA in the USA is one of the most comprehensive and far reaching, and was intended to set up a national policy on the **protection and restoration of environmental quality**. It gave the Federal Government the responsibility to:

> 'create and maintain conditions under which man and nature can exist in productive harmony, and fulfil the social, economic and other requirements of present and future generations of Americans.'
> (Quoted in Glasson *et al.*, 1994.)

The Government should attempt to do this through federal plans and actions:

> 'consistent with other essential considerations of national policy.'

In early drafts of the legislation, it was proposed that it include a statement that:

> 'each person has a fundamental and inalienable right to a healthful environment'

but this was weakened in the actual legislation to the statement that:

> 'each person should enjoy a healthful environment.'

❑ What major differences can you see between the general tenor of NEPA and the UK Department of Environment's definition of EIA?

■ The NEPA requirement is much more wide-ranging; EIA as defined in the UK is a part of the planning process of (some) new developments, whereas the implications of NEPA are that environmental considerations should be a fundamental part of Government action.

An environmental impact statement should not concern only negative impacts of a new development. Some developments may well have less impact than existing practice, and this needs to be recorded. The issues underlying the different perceptions and roles of EIA in different cultures are fascinating, but beyond the scope of this Course.

Figure 3.1 gives one outline of the process and Table 3.1 overleaf gives some of the outputs that would be expected in the report which forms a substantial part of an EIA.

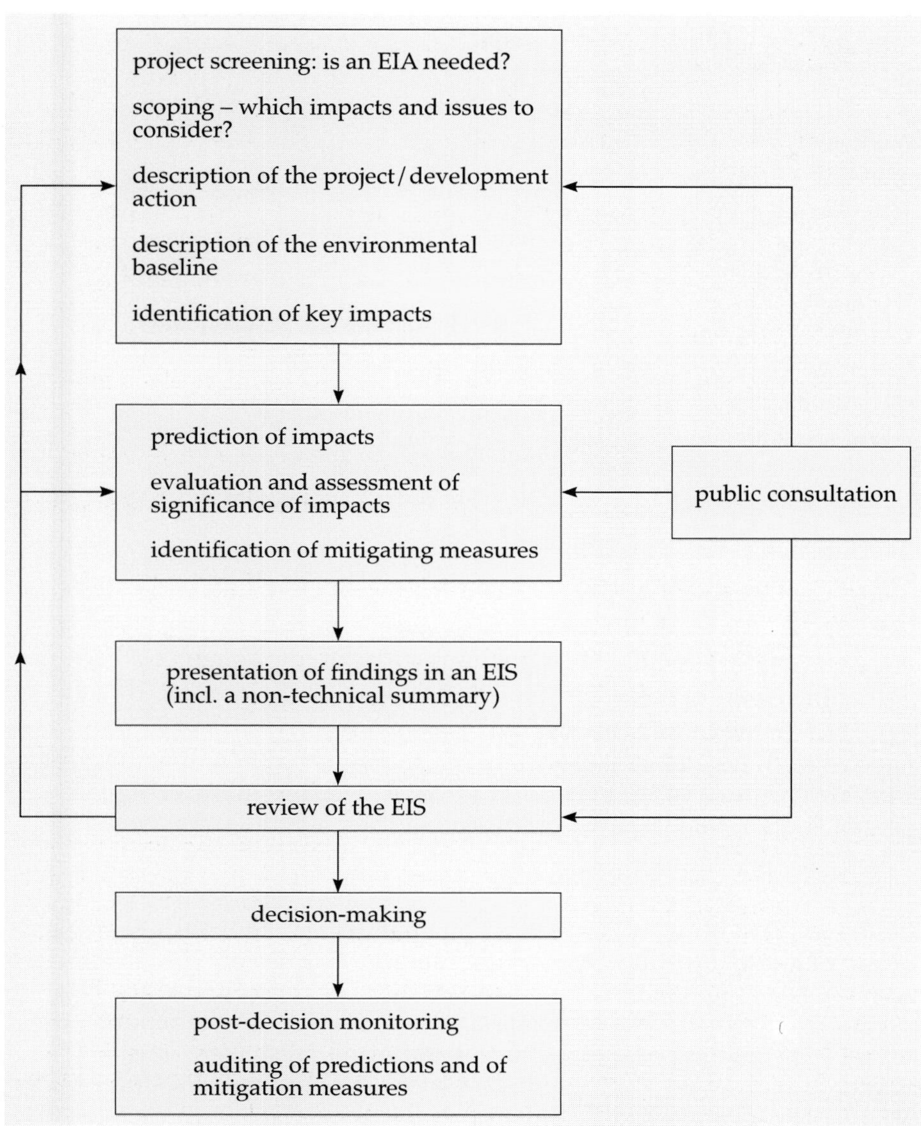

Figure 3.1 An outline of the stages in the process of Environmental Impact Analysis.

Table 3.1 Topics which would be expected to appear in the report of an Environmental Impact Assessment for a proposed development. (Based on Glasson *et al*., 1994.)

Methods and key issues	methods
	summary of key issues
	monitoring programme
Background	need, alternatives, sites
	site description, baseline conditions
	description of proposed development
	construction activities and programme
EIA topic areas	land use, landscape and visual quality
	geology, topography and soils
	hydrology and water quality
	air quality and climate
	ecology; terrestrial and aquatic
	noise
	transport
	socio-economic
	interrelationships between effects

Several of the topics listed in Table 3.1 require ecological skills and knowledge. Skills in field survey are needed for both the initial description of the **environmental baseline**, and for **post-decision monitoring**. Identification of key impacts, prediction of these and identification of mitigating measures all depend on an understanding of ecological principles.

Spellerberg and Minshull undertook an analysis for the British Ecological Society of a total of 64 Environmental Impact Analyses and Environmental Assessments conducted in the UK in 1989 and 1990 (Spellerberg, 1994). Information from surveys of plants was found in 78% of the reports but only 47% contained any animal survey data, and these were mostly concerned with birds. Even these data were, in many cases, simply species lists and often incomplete. Evaluation of the areas concerned was usually subjective in terms of general **nature conservation value** and the criteria for this evaluation were not spelled out. Predictions of impact were made largely on a subjective basis using terms such as 'likely' and 'possibly', with formal assessment of impacts only in 16% of the reports.

Some criticism is almost inevitable given the extent of ecological knowledge and the time-scales over which these types of analyses have to be undertaken, i.e. usually of the order of months, weeks or even days, rather than years. In addition to the problems of obtaining information, there is a serious problem in presentation. A comprehensive EIA would analyse and present the potential effects of several possible configurations of a new development on a number of habitats, each one containing a range of communities and an even larger range of species. One American method of presentation is the **Leopold matrix**. This comprises some 100 possible **project actions** as columns, and over 80 rows of **environmental elements** that may be affected by these actions. The actions include such items as:

- introduction of exotic flora or fauna;
- alteration of groundwater hydrology;
- farming;
- ranching;
- urbanization;
- metallurgical industry;
- landfill.

The environmental elements include physical and chemical characteristics such as land form, soils, water quality, biological conditions (such as flora, fauna, endangered species and barriers/corridors) and cultural factors (which include scenic views, population density, waste disposal and health and safety.) There is also a subgroup of 'ecological relationships' with topics such as salinization of water resources, eutrophication, food chains and brush encroachment.

It is claimed that any one project is likely to involve 20–50 possible interactions between items in columns and those in the rows. For each identified interaction, the analyst is supposed to rate the likely interaction for its **magnitude** and **significance**, each on a scale of 1–10. The magnitude of any particular interaction is the scale on which it occurs, while its significance measures its importance. So, building 500 houses on an area of intensive arable land might have a high magnitude, but low significance, whereas spilling a can of insecticide into a stream flowing through a **Site of Special Scientific Interest** (**SSSI**) might be of low magnitude, but high significance.

Despite its apparent comprehensiveness and precision, there are reasons to doubt the value of such an exercise. First, the categories of environmental elements are so general as to be almost meaningless, and the judgements involved in apportioning values to the magnitude and significance of interactions are extremely subjective. Secondly, even if it is possible to restrict the likely set of interactions to a 20–50 range as suggested, how can the resulting 40–100 numbers be interpreted? This conflict between comprehensiveness and comprehensibility appears to be a fundamental difficulty in EIA.

Despite these limitations, use of EIA should at least expose more of the consequences of development than did earlier planning law. Although at the time of writing they do not have legal enforcement, a series of standards for **Environmental Management Systems** has also been under development in Europe. The first of these was the draft British Standard BS 7750 in 1992, which was followed and paralleled by the development of a Europe-wide standard, the ISO 14 000 series. Figure 3.2 illustrates the major elements in the process which a company has to ensure takes place in order to claim that its activities conform to the British Standard; the ISO standard is broadly similar and compatible. Much of the detail in the standards refers to management actions and documentation within a company but the standards do attempt to define environmental effects.

Figure 3.2 The process required for achieving BS 7750.

In BS 7750, an environmental effect is defined as:

> 'any direct or indirect impingement of the activities, products and services of the organisation upon the environment, whether adverse or beneficial'

which in itself seems to be little more than a tautology although it does note that effects are not necessarily adverse. It goes on to detail some of the effects, including:

- controlled and uncontrolled emissions to atmosphere;
- controlled and uncontrolled discharges to water;
- solid and other wastes;
- contamination of land;
- use of land, water, fuels and energy, and other natural resources;
- noise, odour, dust, vibration and visual impact;
- effects on *specific parts of the environment, including ecosystems* [my italics].

Hunt and Johnson (1995) presented a 'checklist to help identify environmental effects', which is reproduced as Table 3.2.

Table 3.2 Checklist to help identify environmental effects. (Data from Hunt and Johnson, 1995.)

Air	**Water**
global warming	oxygen demand
ozone layer	hydrocarbon spills
acid emissions	eutrophication
ground-level ozone	hazardous substances
hazardous gases/fumes	hazardous organisms
smoke	acidification
radioactivity/radiation	thermal discharges
	radioactivity
Land	foaming, colour, litter
hazardous waste	taste
radioactive waste	water usage
non-hazardous waste	ecosystem disturbance
site contamination	
disturbance	**Nuisance**
soil erosion	visual
	dust
Resource usage	odour
minerals/raw materials	noise, vibration
energy	
fuels	
stock exploitation	

It remains to be seen how widespread these standards become, but combined with **Life Cycle Analysis** (which looks at the impact of a product throughout the system shown in Figure 2.8) they should help to limit or reduce the impact of industrial activity on the environment.

Summary of Section 3.1

- During the 1990s, Environmental Impact Assessment has increasingly been required as part of the process of control of developing human activities.
- The process is complex and methods vary between different countries.
- Identification of impacts, their measurement and assessment of their importance are all difficult and many analyses appear to have weak ecological underpinning.
- A related development is the introduction of standards for Environmental Management Systems, which may reduce the impact of human activities.

Question 3.1 *(Objectives 3.1–3.3)*

Taking as an example an activity with which you are familiar and using Table 3.2 as a guide, list the environmental effects of that activity in a form that could be used to set up a system to manage its environmental impact. (Possible examples might include managing your garden, some part of your job, or a leisure activity such as cycling.)

3.2 Controlling pollution: the need to identify the culprits

A major feature of environmental management systems is identifying and predicting the ecological effect of **polluting** discharges. This reflects our increased awareness of the undesirable effects of a range of materials if they are present in the wrong concentrations and the wrong place. However, incriminating something as a pollutant is not always as easy as it may first appear.

3.2.1 Majority verdict guilty – DDT

Until the mid-1940s, **malaria** was still a serious problem in many areas of Europe as well as in the more commonly recognized danger zones. Although a range of insecticides had been tried, including arsenic salts and pyrethrins (extracted from *Pyrethrum* spp.), none was particularly satisfactory. The discovery of DDT (dichloro-diphenyl-tricholoro-ethane) seemed to be the answer, since it was an effective, persistent poison for insects including the malaria-carrying mosquito *Anopheles maculipennis*, and appeared to have either zero or negligible toxicity to humans. Extensive tests over a long period failed to find evidence of human toxicity, although there are disputed cases where doses in excess of 20 g may have caused death. Doses between 16 and 300 mg kg bodyweight^{-1} in humans caused vomiting and short term convulsions, but daily doses of 1.5 mg kg bodyweight^{-1} over six months or 0.25 mg kg bodyweight^{-1} over 25 years produced no detectable effects. Sales of DDT world-wide were enormous and large numbers of lives were saved by its use, to say nothing of the savings made by the reduced severity of illness and in losses of crops to insects.

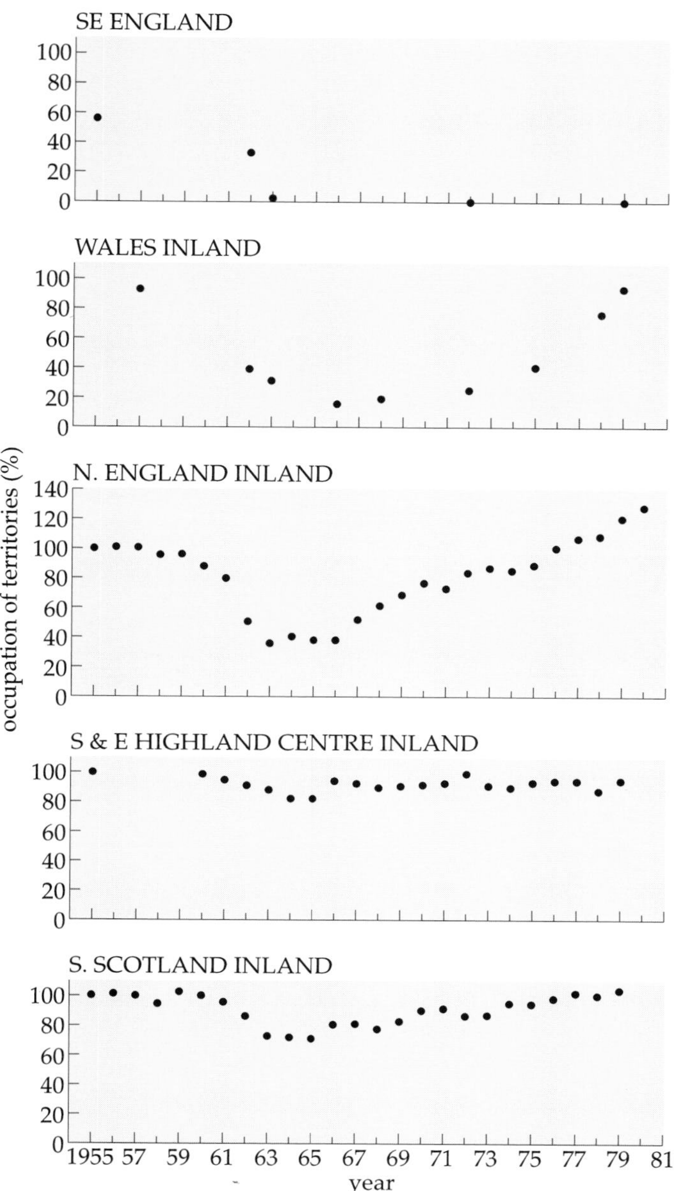

Figure 3.3 Numbers of peregrine falcons in different areas of the UK during the post-war period. Occupation of territories is expressed as a % of the 1930-39 population level.

However, during the period when DDT was being most widely used (1940–1960), it was noted that there was a decrease in the numbers of a range of raptors, including the peregrine falcon (*Falco peregrinus*). The pattern of decline in numbers of falcons in the UK is shown in Figure 3.3, which indicates that the reduction in numbers began in Southern England, and the trend spread north during the 1950s. Given the low mammalian toxicity of DDT, it is surprising that a connection between this decline and DDT usage was even considered. However, Ratcliffe (1980) noted that one of the reasons for the decline was a marked reduction in breeding success, associated with a high frequency of breakages of eggs in the nest. By examining the thickness of eggshells in a wide range of egg collections, Ratcliffe produced the graph shown in Figure 3.4 overleaf, which indicates a fairly clear reduction in eggshell thickness around the period when DDT was first used extensively. Similar findings were confirmed for North American raptors, and a statistically significant relationship between body levels of DDE (a stable breakdown product of DDT) and eggshell thickness was found in several species. Difficulties in rearing raptors in captivity meant that few studies were able to demonstrate unequivocally that DDE was causing the thinning (domestic chickens are apparently not affected in the same way). However, eventually, sufficient evidence was accumulated to suggest that DDT use should be severely restricted.

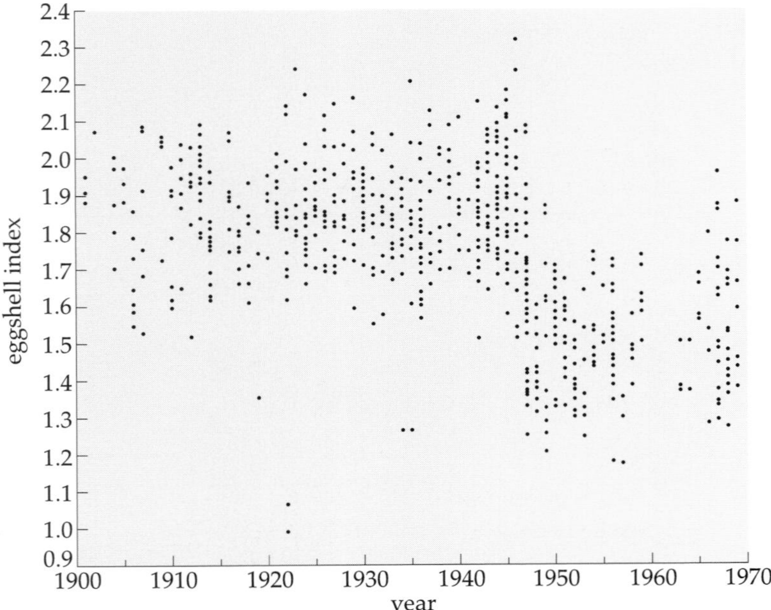

Figure 3.4 Eggshell thicknesses of peregrine falcon eggs from collections of different dates (between 1900 and 1970).

Raptors were severely affected because DDE is fat soluble and, rather than being excreted, accumulates in the fatty tissues of animals that eat it. This accumulation was amplified between trophic levels, because of the ratio of consumption to bodyweight between successive levels. The raptors, at the top of their particular food chain, accumulated the highest levels of DDE. Since the 1970s, the use of DDT has been severely restricted and peregrine numbers have recovered, as shown in the right-hand side of Figure 3.3, which provides the best confirmation of the proposed relationship.

The case against DDT has been generally accepted, although there are still those who regard the restriction on its use as being an over-reaction. By reducing the incidence of malaria, it did provide enormous benefits to human health, but recent studies have suggested that it may affect hormonal relationships in humans, and that infants exposed to high concentrations of DDE in breast milk suffer from reduced reflex responses (Rogan *et al.*, 1986). The balance of the debate is probably still tilted against DDT use but it raises some interesting ethical questions as to whether a beneficial substance which 'only' affects birds of prey should be banned.

3.2.2 Acid rain and tree canopies

During the 1970s, a major preoccupation across Europe and North America was the perceived decline in the health of forest trees. This was particularly severe in parts of the Black Forest area of Germany, where the specific term *waldsterben* ('forest death') was coined and in parts of the then Soviet bloc, such as Czechoslovakia. Over the same period, evidence was growing that pH levels in some lakes were falling, especially in afforested areas in Scandinavia, in parts of the USA and also in Wales and Scotland. This has been identified as **anthropogenic acidification** (Book 1, Chapter 4), arising from the emission of sulphur and nitrogen oxides during the combustion of fossil fuels, their solution in rainwater and subsequent deposition. A simultaneous decline in fish populations has been associated with the change in pH. Figures 3.5 and 3.6 illustrate some of the evidence on which these suggestions were based.

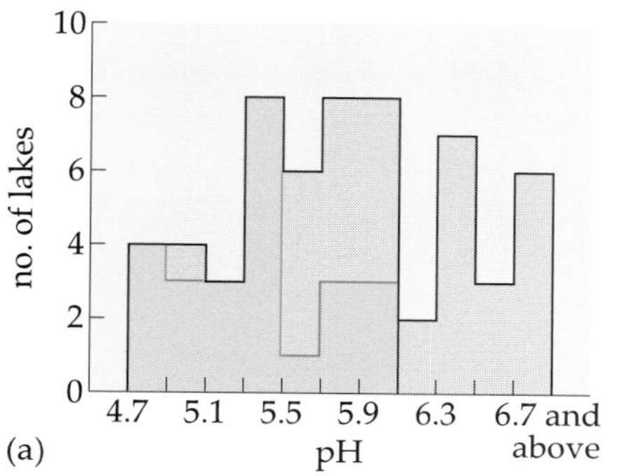

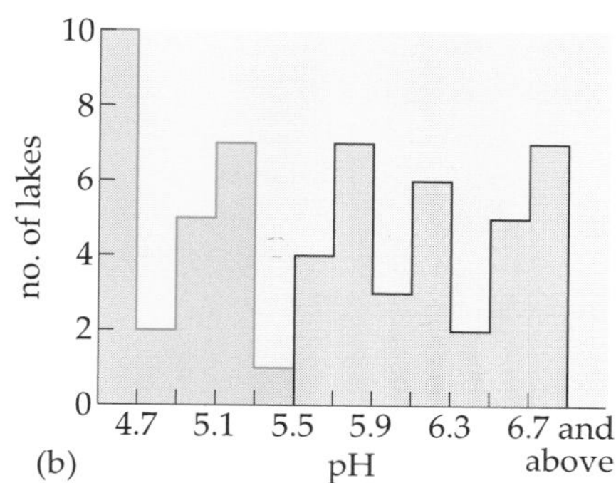

Figure 3.5 The pH distribution of 59 lakes in Sorlandet, Norway, sampled (a) between 1926 and 1953 and (b) again between 1974 and 1976. Coloured areas are those lakes with recent measurements below pH 5.5.

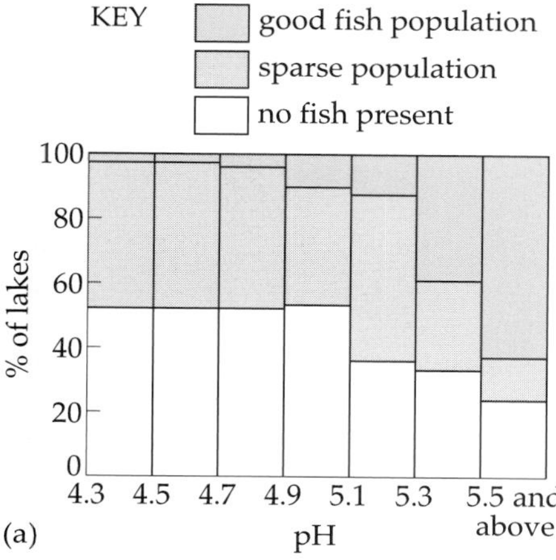

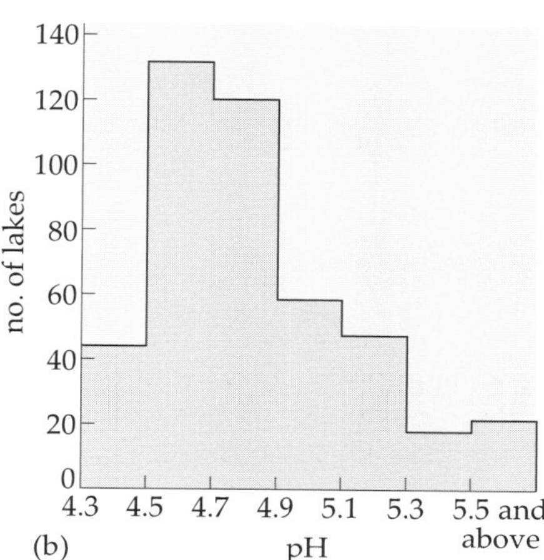

Figure 3.6 (a) The relationship between pH levels and the percentage of lakes that are overpopulated or contain satisfactory fish populations, those with sparse populations and those with no fish, for lakes in Sorlandet which are at an elevation of more than 200 m above sea-level. (b) The numbers of lakes in each pH category.

❑ What change in pH occurred in the sampled lakes?

■ Of the 59 lakes sampled, more lakes (24) had a low pH (<5.3) at the later sampling date, than previously (11) . The distribution of pH shown in Figure 3.5 includes lakes on glacial drifts as well as those on granite bed rock, and a further analysis showed that the pH of lakes on drift had not changed greatly.

❑ Why should lakes on drift not exhibit such large changes in pH?

■ Presumably, the drift material comprised more easily weathered rock which buffered these lakes against pH change. The overall change in pH was 0.11 units, but for the sample of lakes on granite bed rock it was 0.45 units.

❑ What is the apparent relationship between pH levels and fish population?

■ Figure 3.6 suggests that satisfactory fish populations are usually found in lakes with a pH level above 5.3. This is supported by evidence from physiological studies where a low pH level is associated with damage to fish gills and other tissues. These tissue effects have been shown to be due to the presence of aluminium (Al^{3+}) ions in solution at low pH, rather than a direct effect of pH *per se*.

These data and the diatom studies described in Book 1, Chapter 4, do not indicate why acidification occurred. All coastal areas receive some sulphate and chloride from sea spray which has a constant sulphate : chloride ratio. In many of the lakes studied, this ratio was different from that of incoming spray. Figure 3.7 shows the relationship between lake pH and the excess sulphate present, i.e. that in excess of the amount expected from the chloride concentration.

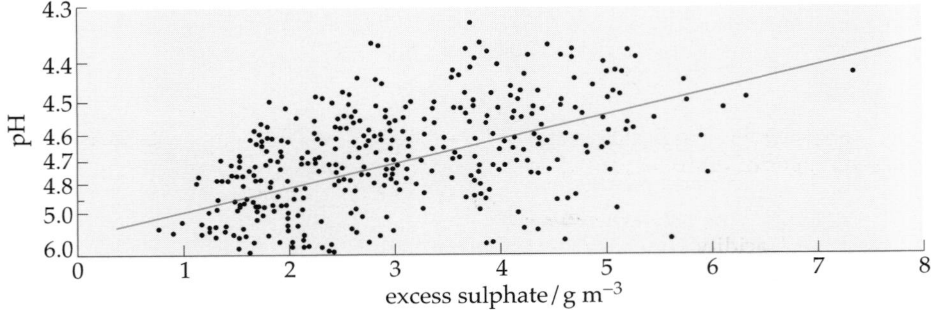

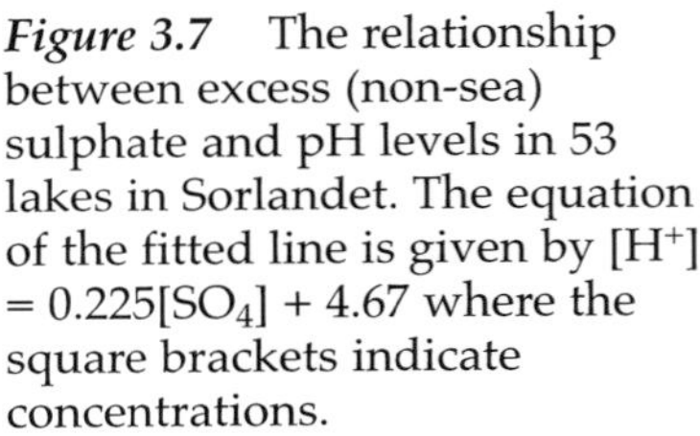
Figure 3.7 The relationship between excess (non-sea) sulphate and pH levels in 53 lakes in Sorlandet. The equation of the fitted line is given by $[H^+] = 0.225[SO_4] + 4.67$ where the square brackets indicate concentrations.

❑ To what extent does Figure 3.7 support the hypothesis that the decline in pH levels was the result of sulphate deposition?

■ There is considerable scatter about the fitted line, but the relationship between additional sulphate and pH is significant. This is, however, only evidence of an association between elevated sulphate levels and reduced pH. To be sure that the effect was due to sulphate deposited from rain, it would be necessary to carry out detailed studies of the sulphur balance for each lake. Such studies in the USA are reported to have cost about $0.5 billion.

The role of sulphur dioxide that originates from industry and electricity generation in the UK, Germany and possibly Holland, in causing acidification of lakes is now generally accepted. The Scandinavian countries are singularly unlucky in their combination of geology, i.e. with a large proportion of acidic rock, and a location that is downwind of major industrial areas. Evidence from diatom studies shows that the observed effects may have been more obvious because of an earlier stage of human influence. Figure 3.8 shows the changes in pH over a 12 000-year period, estimated from diatom assemblages in a sample of lakes in Sweden. From this, it can be seen that during the period from 12 000 BP (Before Present) to 2000 BP, pH levels in the lakes had been falling steadily, but then rose sharply from that period to the beginning of the recent acidification. This rise was attributed to increased erosion of base-rich materials from land disturbed by agriculture, as indicated by Figure 3.9. The subsequent rapid decline in pH levels, associated with increased industrial activity in Europe, might have been less evident had there not been this earlier period of increasing pH values.

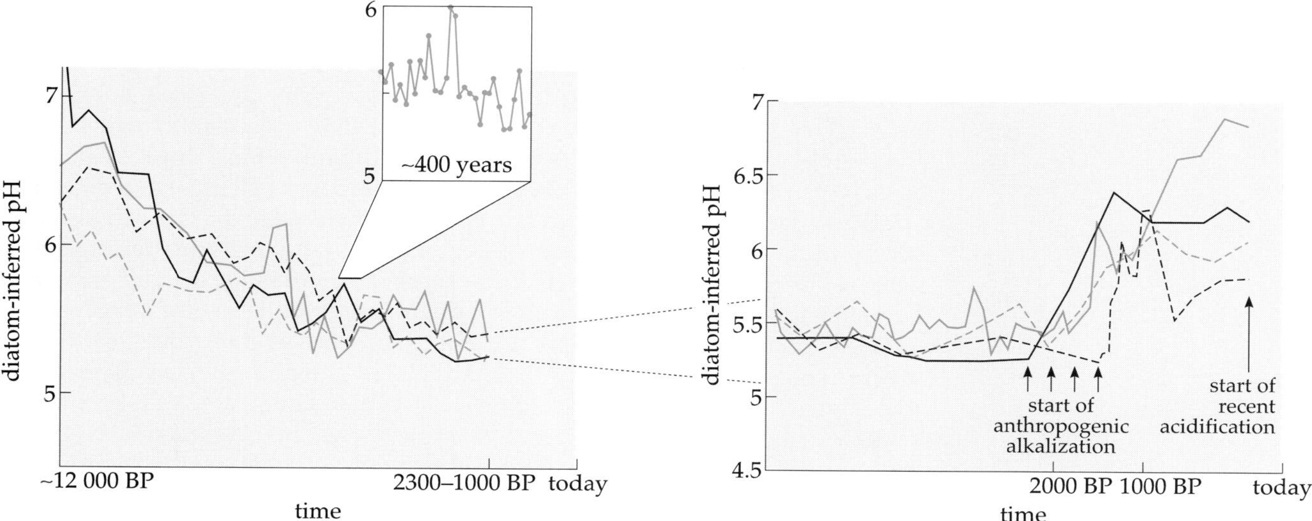

Figure 3.8 Changes in the pH levels of lakes in Southern Sweden, as indicated by the assemblages of diatoms identified in the lake sediments.

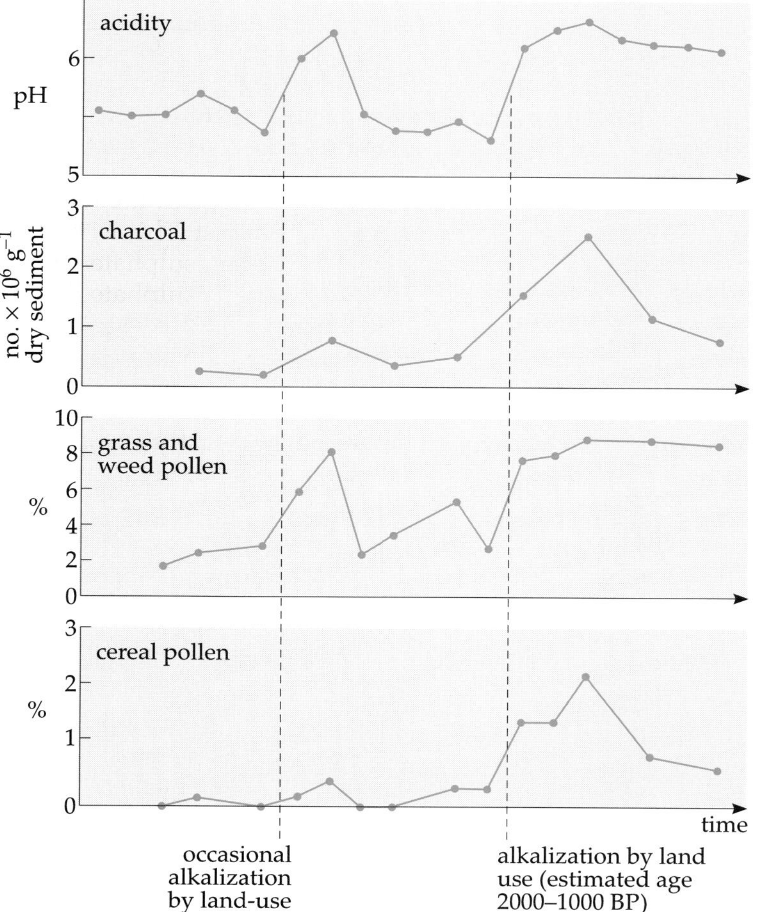

Figure 3.9 The relationship between lake water pH levels and land-use activities indicated by charcoal and pollen analysis. (Charcoal is measured as no. of particles.)

The general agreement to reduce sulphur emissions led to European Union legislation (the Large Plant Combustion Directive). Coal-fired power stations were a major source of sulphur dioxide emissions, so **flue gas desulphurization** equipment has been fitted to those coal-fired stations still in use in the UK and there has been a switch to the use of gas turbines, fired by low sulphur natural gas, for new electricity generating capacity.

Sulphur dioxide in the atmosphere causes respiratory problems in humans, and high SO_2 levels are marked by the loss of lichen species. However, there is still dispute as to whether the gas is the universal cause of the observed *waldsterben*. One possible source of evidence is the establishment of correlations between the extent of damage to trees and local levels of pollution. In practice, obtaining this evidence is not so simple. First, since trees are long-lived, it is essential that records extend over a long period. The available records of atmospheric pollution are patchy, use varying methods of analysis and cover different pollutants on different sites for different lengths of time. Only since about 1985 have there been agreed, and internationally comparable, measures of tree canopy health. Secondly, a whole range of features of the environment may be **intercorrelated**. This makes it difficult to establish which, if any, has a **causal** effect rather than simply varying in the same way as the observed effect. One major examination of pollution effects on tree health was carried out by the Forest Authority in the UK, who had been monitoring forest health over an extended period, and reported results in 1994. Species examined were: Norway spruce *Picea abies* (L). Karst., sitka spruce *Picea sitchensis* (Bong.) Carr., Scots pine *Pinus sylvestris* L., beech *Fagus sylvatica* L., oak *Quercus petraea* (Mattuschka) Lieblein, *Q. robur* L. and their hybrids). The crown density of the trees was estimated visually. Browning and yellowing of current and older leaves, and overall discoloration of the sampled trees, was assessed. Pollution and meteorological data were obtained either by local monitoring, or by using mathematical models of the geographic variation in pollution levels.

These forest condition data were recorded between 1989 and 1992. The samples chosen were shown to be a reasonable statistical representation of the environments encountered by these species in the UK. Results suggested that, overall, the biggest single factor affecting tree condition was **drought**. Very little of the observed change in tree health could be attributed to the estimated levels of pollution, except for dieback in beech and the extent of flowering in Scots pine, both of which were related to ground-level ozone, and crown density in Norway spruce which was associated with sulphur deposition.

Although these results suggest that there may be some link between air pollution and tree health, air pollution accounted for less than 5% of the variation in health. In addition to the limitations already considered, the authors also noted that they had not been able to take into account the considerable effects of mechanical damage (that due to wind, snow and storms) on forest condition. They suggested that this was a major limitation of the work, because sulphur deposition tends to be highest in elevated and exposed areas, and any effect which was supposed to be due to sulphur might just be due to mechanical damage.

Their conclusion was that:

> 'The results (which are entirely consistent with earlier work reported by the Forestry Authority) indicate that although pollution may be a factor in influencing the health of British trees, with respect to the general condition of trees throughout Britain the role of pollution is probably small. The analysis described in this report cannot establish a causal link between pollution and the forest condition.'

This rather negative conclusion has not prevented other experimental work being carried out on the links between air quality and tree condition, but the results of this study serve mainly to highlight the complexity of the interactions.

Something of this can be illustrated by a study on the indirect effects of elevated levels of sulphur dioxide on spruce. Two needle fungi, *Lophodermium piceae* and *Rhizosphacra kalkhoffii*, are associated with premature senescence of spruce needles. Comparison of the extent of infection with *R. kalkhoffii* on two sites in South Wales with differing levels of pollution showed that there was a higher degree of infection at the more heavily polluted site. A separate experiment in which open-grown sitka spruce trees were fumigated with varying amounts of sulphur dioxide showed that *R. kalkhoffii* colonization in the open air was enhanced by increased levels of fumigation. However, treatment with an aphicide (i.e. a pesticide that killed aphids – in this case the aphid *Elatobium abietum*) produced the results shown in Figure 3.10.

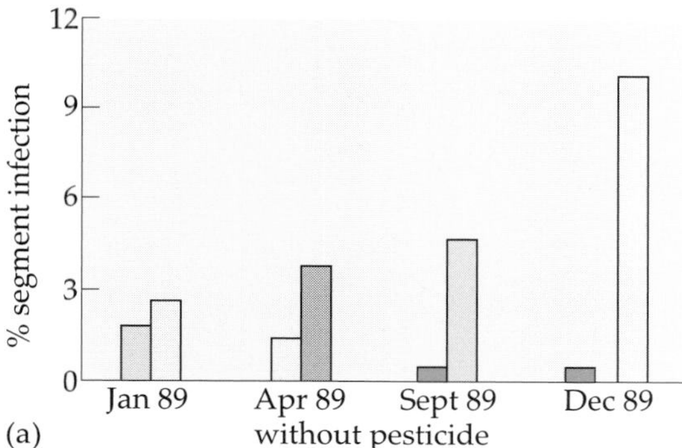

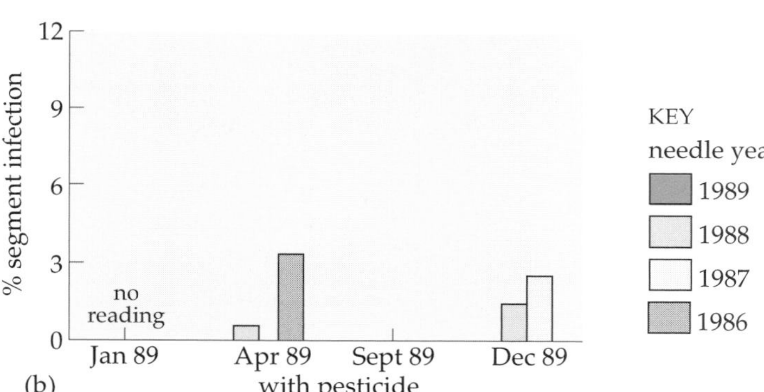

Figure 3.10 The effect of an aphicide on the percentage colonization of sitka spruce by the fungus *Lophodermium piceae* at a highly polluted site in South Wales. The needle year is the year in which particular needles formed and is therefore an indication of their age.

❑ What are the implications of Figure 3.10?

■ There are two possibilities. Either the aphicide actually had some direct effect on the fungus, or the aphids (which presumably were reduced in numbers by the aphicide) were having a positive effect on infection by the fungus.

The currently accepted picture is that very high levels of sulphur dioxide, in association with other pollutants, have been the direct cause of tree damage in parts of Central Europe and Poland. However, the route from cause to effect can involve a number of stages, as suggested in Figure 3.11.

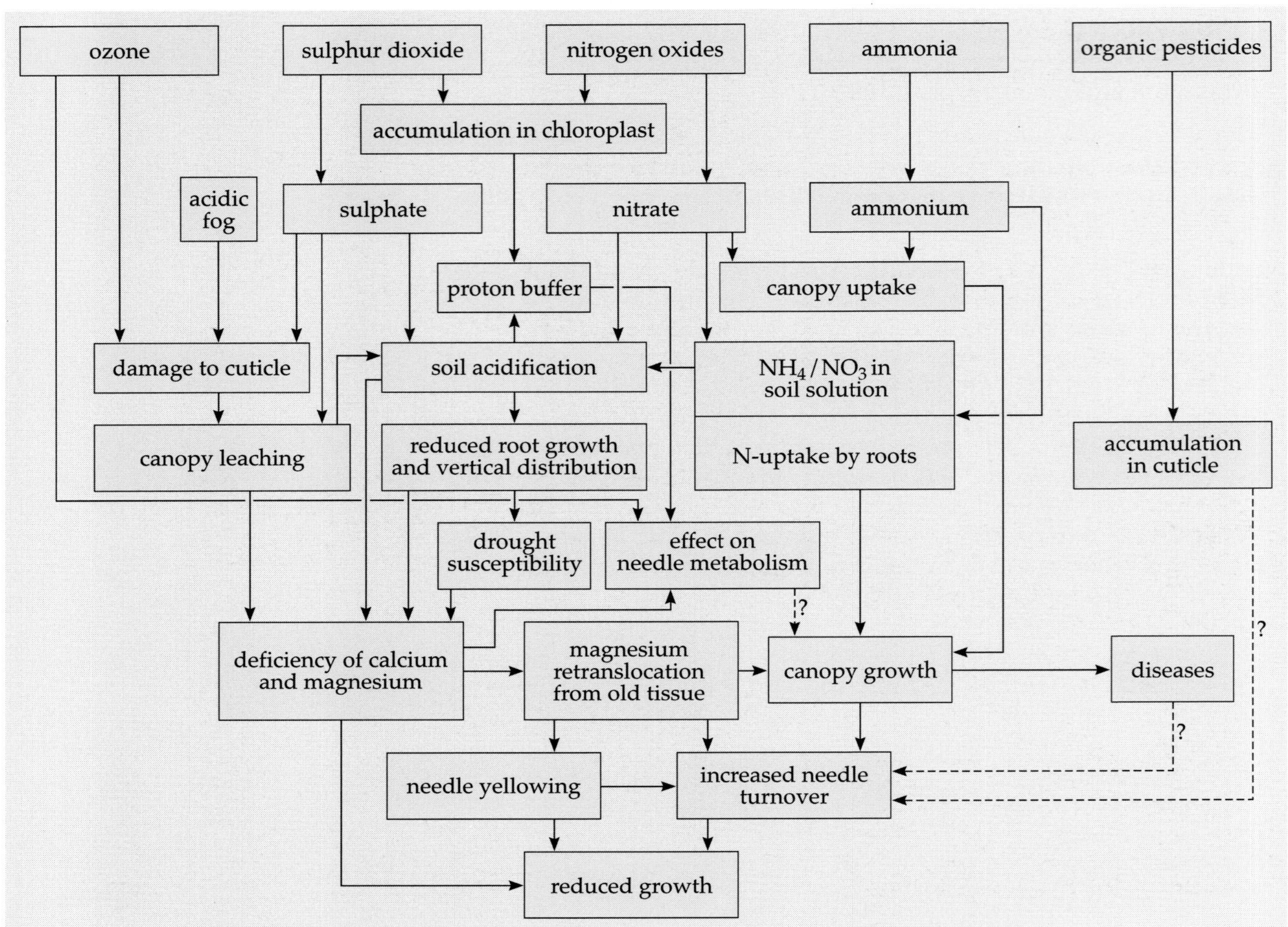

Figure 3.11 The links between a range of factors and tree damage.

Ozone and volatile organic compounds are currently another centre of attention. The chemistry of these in the atmosphere is complex, and is influenced by the intensity of solar radiation, so that there remains a lot of work to be done in disentangling the outcomes. Even sulphur dioxide can have some beneficial effects, as Figure 3.12 suggests.

HARVEST 1969

HARVEST 1989

SPRING '91

SPRING '92

SULPHUR SPRAY

HARVEST '92

SPRING '93

ICI SULPHUR ·GOLD

HARVEST 1993

The industrial clean up hasn't been good news for everyone, as arable farmers who are now seeing the effects of sulphur deficiency will tell you.

Crops such as oilseed rape and winter wheat are the first to show characteristic yield loss and grain quality problems.

It's just as well that ICI Fertilizers developed 'SULPHUR-GOLD', a nitrogen and sulphur blended fertilizer formulated to provide a practical and cost-effective solution to sulphur deficiency.

CONTACT YOUR LOCAL ICI DISTRIBUTOR NOW FOR DETAILS OF SULPHUR-GOLD SPECIAL OFFERS

FOR OILSEED RAPE AND WINTER WHEAT

THERE REALLY IS NO ALTERNATIVE TO

Fertilizers

Figure 3.12 An advertisement for sulphur-containing fertilizers.

Summary of Section 3.2

- Many of the impacts of human activity are the result of the discharge of polluting materials, but it is necessary to identify precisely what material is causing an observed effect, and how.
- Identification of effects is difficult because of correlations between different variables and the absence of appropriate experimental observations.
- In the case of DDT, the deleterious effects on higher level carnivores have been generally accepted, but the relationship between forest damage ('waldsterben') and atmospheric pollution is still disputed.
- Identification of a pollution effect still leaves open the question of whether benefits to humans from the possible pollutant are commensurate with any damage caused.

Question 3.2 *(Objective 3.4)*

Patch spraying of DDT was widely used in Zimbabwe for control of tsetse fly (*Glossina* spp.) prior to its banning in 1985. An extensive programme of environmental impact assessment was conducted by the UK Natural Resources Institute for the Zimbabwean Government in the period 1989–90. Table 3.3 shows the sighting rates of lizard species in sprayed and unsprayed woodland and Figure 3.13 shows the composition of the lizard fauna in relation to number of spray treatments. All the lizard species examined feed on insects.

Table 3.3 Sightings (per search hour) of the lizard *Mabuya striata* and other lizard species in unsprayed woodland and woodland sprayed with DDT.

Species	Unsprayed	Sprayed	*p*
Mabuya striata	9.9	5.7	< 0.02
other species	3.2	2.2	n.s.

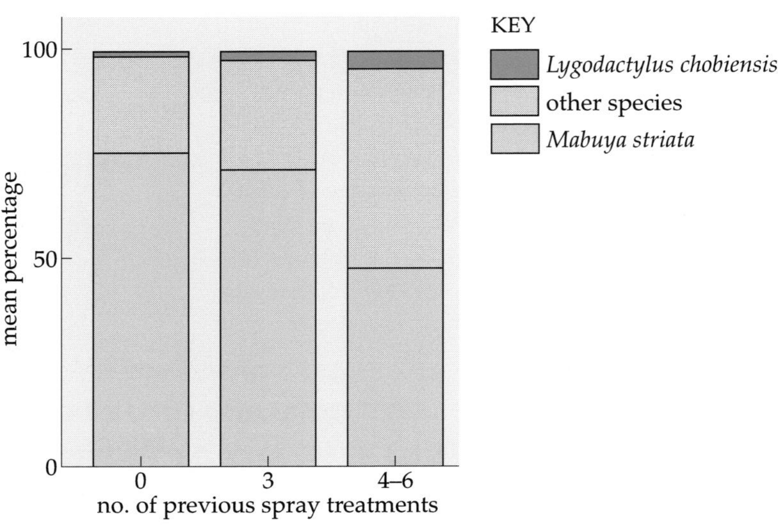

Figure 3.13 Composition of lizard fauna in woodland in Zimbabwe under different spray treatments.

(a) What was the apparent effect of DDT spraying on lizard communities?

(b) Do these results accord with Ratcliffe's studies of raptors with respect to the potential ecological effects of DDT?

Question 3.3 *(Objectives 3.1 & 3.4)*

Table 3.4 shows a range of soil and other factors measured in stands of Norway spruce (*Picea abies*) in Southern Norway, in a 'core area' where there was more than 22% defoliation, and in a peripheral area with less than 6% defoliation. Do the data suggest that air pollution is the cause of the defoliation?

Table 3.4 Soil and other factors in areas of high and low defoliation of Norway spruce (*P. abies*). (Data derived from Nelleman and Frogner, 1994.)

Factor	Defoliation:	
	high	low
Soil		
podsols %	70	76
carbon %	38	38
nitrogen %	1.6	1.3
calcium %	7.0	14.0*
magnesium %	1.7	2.5*
buffering capacity		
% base saturation	46.0	71.0**
Pollution / mmol m^{-2} y^{-1}		
sulphur	83.0	56.0**
nitrate	62.0	43.0**
ammonium	56.0	36.0**
Site		
altitude / m.a.s.l.	198	177*
exposed %	3	1
Productivity (% of total no. of sites in each category)		
low productivity	22	23
medium productivity	65	64
high productivity	13	13

*/** Denote values in rows which differ significantly ($p < 0.05$, $p < 0.001$ respectively).

3.3 Management of exploited species

Using the population dynamic models which you looked at in Book 2, and with adequate data, it might be possible to devise harvesting strategies for whales and other exploited species which allow humans to derive some benefit, without causing undue damage to the populations. If the catch of whales of a given species is to be **sustainable**, then the numbers caught in one year must, on average, equal the intrinsic increase in the whale population in that year. For a model such as the one presented in Chapter 4, Book 2, plotting dN/dt against whale population, N, suggests that dN/dt has a maximum value at an intermediate population size. If the rate of harvesting $h(N)$ exactly equals this maximum value, that would represent the maximum rate of harvesting that could be obtained. Knowing N, and the shape of the curve, it should then be possible to estimate the **Maximum Sustainable Yield**, Y. For a particular species (e.g. the blue whale), N can be estimated, using a method based on catch-per-unit-effort data of the sort given in Figure 1.11.

Figure 3.14 shows values of Y for the blue whale obtained for several different years, plotted against the estimated size of the blue whale population for the same years. A curve has been fitted approximately to the plotted points. Towards the left of the graph, the points fit the curve fairly closely; towards the right, the points are much more scattered, and the curve becomes speculative. Figure 3.14 suggests that the value of Y rises to a peak when the population is about 130 000 and declines thereafter, possibly to zero with a population of over 200 000.

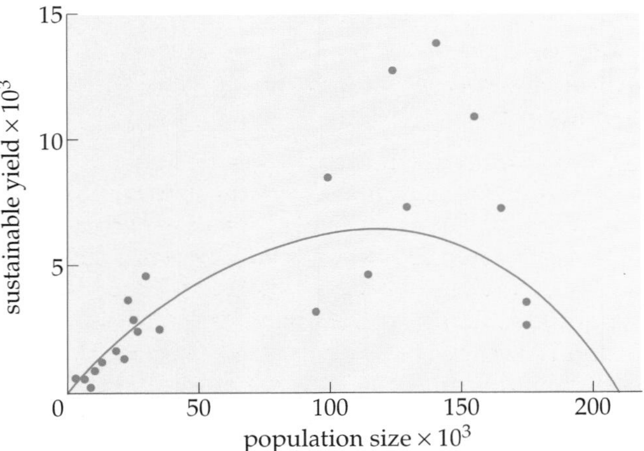

Figure 3.14 Calculated sustainable yield Y of blue whales in the Antarctic.

- ❑ For a blue whale population of about 50 000, derive from Figure 3.14 an estimate of the sustainable yield.

- ■ For a population of about 50 000, the sustainable yield Y is about 4000, i.e. the sustainable yield is about 8% of the size of the exploitable population.

Figure 3.14 suggests that an annual catch of some 6000 blue whales could be sustained from a population of about 120 000. However, Figure 1.12 showed that from the mid-1920s onwards, annual catches were well above 10 000 per annum. Not surprisingly, this rate of catching was *not* sustainable. If you look at Figure 1.13, you can see that in 1946-50 when catches had dropped (towards 6000, see Figure 1.12), the actual population was still declining.

- ❑ Given the shape of Figure 3.14, why should the blue whale population still have declined when annual catches were only equal to the maximum sustainable yield?

- ■ An annual catch of 6000 is the *maximum* yield that can be sustained. If the model in Figure 3.14 is correct, then a catch of this magnitude from a population greater than 120 000 should reduce that population to about this level, and thereafter this catch rate should be sustainable. If, however, the population was already less than this value, as seems probable given the high catch-rates prior to 1940, then the population could not possibly sustain a catch rate of 6000, and would decline irretrievably so long as such a catch rate was attempted.

From 1946 onwards, whaling was regulated by the International Whaling Commission (IWC) on the basis of sustainable yield models, but for all three whale species shown in Figure 1.13, it appears that the catch rate had exceeded the maximum sustainable yield (MSY) for long enough to reduce populations well below the level appropriate for MSY. During the 1960s and 1970s, increasing concern was voiced about this situation and, in 1982, the IWC introduced a complete moratorium on commercial whaling from 1985, although with exceptions. Japan retained the right to catch whales 'for research purposes' and hunting was permitted for aboriginal peoples to whom whales represented a significant 'nutritional or cultural resource' (Gambell, 1993). The Commission was expected to make recommendations which would allow resumption of commercial whaling by 1992. In fact, at the time of writing (1995), the Commission had voted to retain the moratorium, although various interests have claimed that the population of minke whales *Balaenoptera acutorostrata*, and possibly others, were sufficient for commercial hunting.

Whales represent a resource without a single owner, but **held in common** and the legal problems for international bodies attempting to control their exploitation are formidable. Hardin (1965) proposed that with a resource held in common, such as an area of common grazing, there arises what he called the **tragedy of the commons.** According to Hardin, each individual grazier tries to graze as many animals as possible on the common, because even if that individual restricted numbers, others would not. If all graziers behave in the same individualistic way, the resource (the grazing) will be **overexploited** and so the performance of the total grazing herd will be reduced. More recent research suggests that most traditional common grazings were subject to strong social or legal restraints on the numbers of animals that could be grazed by any individual. Overgrazing was actually rare, but the idea that common resources are inherently likely to be overexploited has remained politically powerful.

One extension of Hardin's idea has been to claim that overexploitation of a resource is unlikely if that resource is *owned* by a single individual, or a well-defined group of individuals. Unfortunately, the same neoclassical economics that underpins the notions of ownership suggest that it can be **economically rational** for the owner of a population to exploit it to extinction. This hinges on the value of the products from a population today relative to their future use. We generally value even an inflation-proofed benefit of £1000 in ten years' time as being worth less than £1000 today (if only because if we had that £1000 today, we could invest it and earn interest for ten years). This is the basis of the economic practice of **discounting**. Using this argument, Clark (1973) showed that if the **intrinsic percentage rate of increase** (λ) of an exploited population is less than contemporary monetary interest rates, then the maximum total **economic benefit** to the owner (and by extension, to society) would be obtained by hunting the exploited species to extinction as rapidly as possible. To oversimplify the argument, if 100 of the animals today are worth 100 units, and the percentage rate of increase is five units per annum, then left alone, they will be worth 105 units in a year's time. If they were all slaughtered, and the proceeds invested at an interest rate of 10%, then at the end of the year, the hunter has 110 units. Only if the percentage rate of increase is greater than monetary interest rates is it 'rational' to leave the population to breed.

Judged solely on economic criteria, the preceding argument is perfectly logical. We can still question whaling on ethical grounds, as we have no obvious and inalienable *right* to use or eliminate other species. We can also question the purely economic argument, since it assumes that everyone accepts this reducing valuation of future benefits. The observed behaviour of the majority of consumers does fit this model, but recent discussion of the concept of **sustainable development** suggests that this could change. Sustainable development was originally defined in the 1987 report of the World Commission on Environment and Development, chaired by Norway's then Prime Minister, Gro Harlem Brundtland, and frequently referred to as the 'Brundtland Commission'. Various subsequent definitions have been used, of which the following is typical:

> 'development that meets the needs of the present without compromising the ability of future generations to meet their own needs.'

It will be interesting to see the extent to which this concept is adopted as a guide to policy in the future.

Summary of Section 3.3

- Models of population dynamics of exploited species suggest that it is theoretically possible to determine a harvesting regime which provides the maximum sustainable yield for humans from that population.
- Evidence from marine mammal populations suggests that the rates of harvesting employed have regularly exceeded sustainable levels.

- Economic models can be used to suggest that it is economically rational to exceed sustainable rates of harvesting, and to hunt populations to extinction.
- Some of these arguments have been questioned, and the concept of 'sustainable development' has been proposed as a guideline.

Question 3.4

(Objective 3.6)

A model of the population dynamics of red deer on Rhum was devised to suggest strategies for obtaining the maximum sustainable yield of 'trophies' (stags more than five years old) and of hinds (Clutton Brock and Lonergan, 1994). This model assumed that the numbers of deer calves born, surviving the first winter, deer surviving as yearlings through the second winter and adults surviving each year were all density dependent, and that it was the density of hinds that was the most important factor. Figure 3.15 shows the effect of different culling regimes for females on the numbers of deer in different classes at equilibrium. The numbers are scaled to a population of 1000 hinds before culling.

(a) Summarize the data in Figure 3.15.

(b) The culling rate for hinds in Scotland is usually around 7%. Assuming that all the stags aged five years or over are culled each year, is this the optimum culling rate for hinds?

(c) Estimate the optimum hind culling rate.

(d) How confident would you be in recommending such a culling rate to the manager of a deer park?

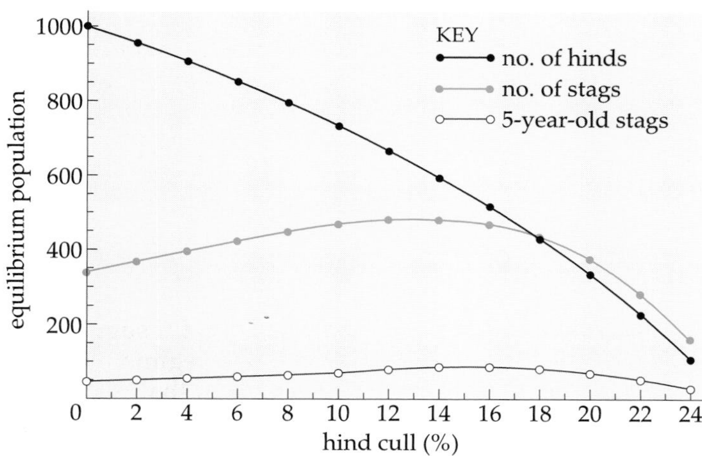

Figure 3.15 Numbers of hinds and stags of different age categories (hinds = all animals ≥ 1 year old; stags = ≥ 1 year old) expected at equilibrium before the onset of the annual cull.

3.4 Managing derelict land

In the UK, some 68 000 ha of land is officially classified as derelict. Such classification is the subject of some controversy, and other estimates of the area of derelict land have been as high as 340 000 ha. The land involved has usually been used for industrial operations, such as the tipping of colliery or mineral working spoil, dumping of fuel ash from power stations, the extraction of sand or gravel, etc. In addition, official figures hint that a total of 50 000 to 100 000 ha of land may be **contaminated**, that is affected by heavy metals or toxic organic materials. Table 3.5 shows the characteristics of a range of derelict sites.

Table 3.5 The physical and chemical characteristics of different types of derelict land materials (data from Bradshaw and Chadwick, 1980). The key provides a scoring system that allows each material to be assessed relative to the requirements for the establishment of a soil/plant ecosystem on that particular material.

PHYSICAL:

Materials	Texture and structure	Stability	Water supply	Surface temp.
colliery spoil	OOO	OOO/o	O/o	o/+++
strip mining	OOO/o	OOO/o	OO/o	o/+++
fly ash	OO/o	o	o	o
oil shale	OO	OOO/o	OO	o/++
iron ore mining	OOO/o	OO/o	O/o	o
bauxite mining	OO/o	o	o	o
heavy metal wastes	OOO	OOO/o	OO/o	o
gold wastes	OOO	OOO	O	o
china clay wastes	OOO	OO	OO	o
acid rocks	OOO	o	OO	o
calcareous rocks	OOO	o	OO	o
sand and gravel	O/o	o	o	o
coastal sands	OO/o	OOO/o	O/o	o
land from sea	OO	o	o	o
urban wastes	OOO/o	o	o	o
roadsides	OOO/o	OOO	OO/o	O/o

CHEMICAL:

Materials	Macro-nutrients	Micro-nutrients	pH	Toxic materials	Salinity
colliery spoil	OOO	o	OOO/o	o	o/++
strip mining	OOO/o	o	OOO	o	o/++
fly ash	OOO	o	+++	++	++
oil shale	OOO	o	OO/o	o	o/++
iron ore mining	OO	o	o	o	o
bauxite mining	OO	o	o	o	o
heavy metal wastes	OOO	o	OOO/+	+/+++	o/+++
gold wastes	OOO	o	OOO	o	o
china clay wastes	OOO	o	O	o	o
acid rocks	OO	o	O	o	o
calcareous rocks	OOO	o	+	o	o
sand and gravel	O/o	o	O/o	o	o
coastal sands	OOO	o	o	o	o
land from sea	OO	o	o/+	o	+++
urban wastes	OO	o	o	o/++	o
roadsides	OO	o	O/o	o	o/++

KEY for Table 3.5

severe deficit	moderate deficit	slight deficit	adequate	slight excess	moderate excess	severe excess
OOO	OO	O	o	+	++	+++

❑ What appears to be the commonest limitation to growth of vegetation on the forms of derelict land in Table 3.5?

■ Absence of macronutrients. Shortage of nitrogen, phosphorus and potassium is moderate to severe in all the types listed, except sand and gravel workings and some cases of strip mining. The second most common problem appears to be texture and structure of the substrate.

❑ Apart from the physical and chemical limitations to the regrowth of vegetation given in Table 3.5, what other factor might prevent the return of a derelict area to the state it was in prior to its destruction?

■ The availability of propagules of the original species; many of the derelict areas are surrounded by urban land, or areas now devoted to arable agriculture, which form barriers to dispersal.

Potentially, it is possible to overcome all the limitations to the process of **revegetation** using machinery, fertilizer and careful management. Provided we have an adequate understanding of the functioning of the original ecosystem and a source of appropriate genotypes of all species, there is no reason in theory why derelict land should not be restored to exactly the state it was in prior to dereliction. Some of the techniques required for this are listed in Table 3.6.

Table 3.6 The underlying problems of derelict land and their treatment.

Factors		Problem	Short-term treatment	Long-term treatment
PHYSICAL:	structure	too compact	rip or scarify	vegetation
		too open	compact or cover with fine material	vegetation
	stability	unstable	stabilizer/mulch	levelling or vegetation
	moisture	too wet	drain	drain
		too dry	organic mulch	vegetation
NUTRITION:	macro-nutrients	nitrogen	fertilizer	legume
		others	fertilizer + lime	fertilizer + lime
	micro-nutrients	inadequate	fertilizer	fertilizer
TOXICITY:	pH	too high	pyritic waste or organic matter	weathering
		too low	lime	lime
	heavy metals	too high	organic mulch or metal-tolerant cultivar	inert covering, metal-tolerant cultivar, bioremediation*
	salinity	too high	weathering or irrigate	tolerant species or cultivar

*The use of **hyperaccumulator** species which take up large amounts of the heavy metal and can be harvested to remove the pollutant.

❑ What limit is there in practice to the reconstruction of an ecosystem on derelict land?

■ The obvious one is cost; all the treatments listed are likely to be expensive, both in terms of their one-off capital cost, and in continued maintenance.

The cheapest restoration is to rely on succession. Derelict land may be only an extreme version of a disturbed habitat, and some derelict sites exhibit successional changes to what is often regarded as a particularly rich and interesting ecosystem. This has already occurred on waste tips arising from the Leblanc process described earlier in Section 2.4. These now carry a flora of common alkali-tolerant species and some relatively rare orchids, a flora which is not found elsewhere in the region. It has been noted that 75 out of the 3000 SSSIs in the UK are old quarries and other mineral workings. In general, the process of succession is too slow and haphazard to be of direct relevance in the restoration of derelict land, but one cynical observer noted that restoration needs to take place soon after degradation, as the derelict site may otherwise itself become worth preserving!

Each of the major **land consuming industries** in the UK has a maximum area for which it has planning permission to extract material. Table 3.7 shows these permitted areas for 1988, and the percentage of the current permitted areas that had been reclaimed between 1982 and 1988 in England.

Table 3.7 Permitted surface mineral workings in 1988, percentages of current permitted areas reclaimed between 1982 and 1988 and end uses of reclaimed land. (Data from Department of the Environment (1992) *The UK Environment*.)

Use	**Permitted area/ha**	**Percentage reclaimed**
extractable use:		
sand and gravel	28 830	32
limestone	11 532	4
clay / shale	9610	12
open-cast coal	8649	48
deep-mined coal	n.a.	23
industrial sand	n.a.	9
'remainder'	n.a.	5
ironstone	14 415	n.a.
'other minerals'	23 064	n.a.
use after restoration:		
sport, recreation, agriculture / forestry, public open space.	n.a.	63
industry, commerce, housing	n.a.	27
miscellaneous	n.a.	10

Table 3.7 shows that there is a relatively large area of land still in need of restoration in the UK. The following Section looks at one simple example.

3.4.1 China clay wastes

The area round St. Austell in Cornwall has been a source of clay for china manufacture since about 1770. It now represents an industry extracting 3.07×10^6 t annually, with exports of 2.2×10^6 t, worth £24 million in 1991. The clay is extracted from pits, where it occurs mixed with quartz sand, fine micaceous mud and undecomposed rock in the approximate proportions 1 : 6 : 1 : 1. The sand is separated out by washing, and is then tipped on the land around the pits. The mud is settled out in shallow lagoons. The resulting landscape is quite spectacular, as shown in Figure 1.21, and does revegetate slowly. The characteristics of the waste sand and mud are given in Table 3.8 (overleaf).

Table 3.8 Physical characteristics and nutrient supply of waste sand and mica from china clay extractions, compared with a nearby agricultural area. (Data from Bradshaw and Chadwick, 1980.)

Material	Nutrients available/p.p.m.					pH	Particle size/mm				
	N	P	K	Mg	Ca		>2	2–0.2	0.2–0.02	0.020–0.002	<0.002
sand	9	2.0	10	16	85	4.5	56	30	11	2	1
mica	18	2.8	13	20	115	4.0	0	5	44	47	4
agricultural soil	1560	46	176	130	990	4.7	0	1	34	40	25

❑ From Table 3.8, what do you consider to be the most important limitations to vegetation growth on the sand and on the mica? Which is more likely to support reasonable plant growth?

■ All elements are present in much lower concentrations in both materials, than in an agricultural soil; the particle-size distribution in the sands is such that the spoil would hold very little water. Of the nutrients, the relative difference in abundance is greatest for nitrogen, which might be the major limitation. There is no major difference between the wastes in mineral nutrient content. However, the particle size distribution of the mica is much closer to that of agricultural soil. The mica would be expected to have an appreciable cation exchange capacity, so might support vegetation more readily.

❑ Outline an experiment which could be used to test your suggestions.

■ The obvious experiment is to supply a range of ameliorations, such as water and mineral nutrients, singly and in combination, to sown plots of required species, and to assess their performance (see Figure 3.16).

Figure 3.16 A simple fertilizer experiment on china clay waste with added combinations of macro- and micro-nutrients to show that lack of nitrogen alone was preventing growth.

Nutrient addition experiments have shown that the major limitation to vegetation growth on china clay sand is low nitrogen concentrations and the deficit is accentuated by the rapid rate of leaching. Figure 3.17 shows the distribution of nitrogen through the sand profile where nitrate fertilizer was applied to china clay waste. This rapid leaching means that to sustain production of vegetation on china clay sand it is necessary to add nutrients at regular intervals, or to create a pool of nutrients from which leaching is limited, but where mineralization is fast enough not to limit plant growth. One potential source of such a pool is another waste material, sewage sludge. In total, the UK sewage industry produces the equivalent of 135×10^6 t dry weight of sludge per annum and, as noted in Chapter 2, sea dumping is no longer an option for this.

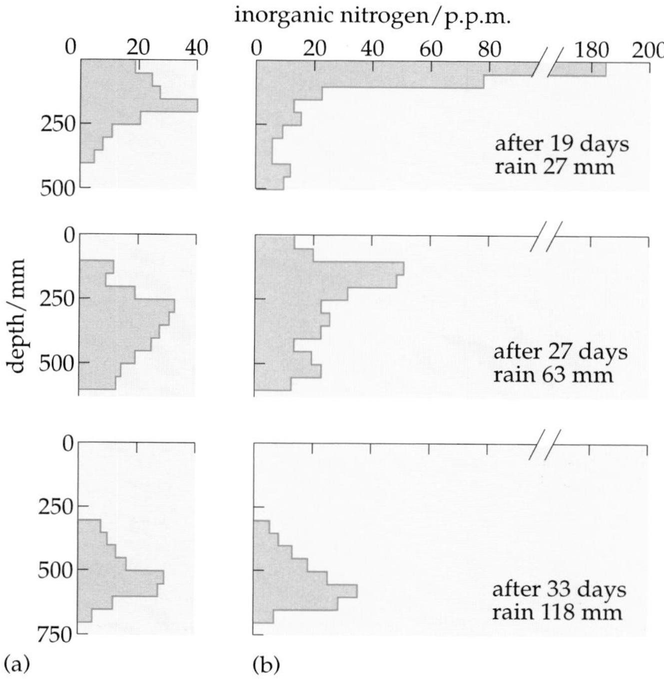

Figure 3.17 Leaching of nutrients on china clay waste. Nitrate fertilizer was added at time of sowing at rates of (a) 125 kg N ha^{-1} and (b) 250 kg N ha^{-1}.

❑ What weight of sludge per hectare would this provide if it were spread over the existing derelict land? Would this be a significant contribution to the organic matter pool of these sites?

■ Assuming there are 68 000 ha of derelict land, the available sludge would provide about almost 2000 dry tonnes per hectare. A typical arable soil has about 50 tonnes of carbon or about 100 tonnes of soil organic matter per hectare, so such an application would be extremely useful.

Where sewage sludge with low heavy metal content is available within reasonable distance of the site for restoration, it is a useful ameliorant for nutrient-poor derelict sites. Another approach involves using species able to fix nitrogen, e.g. alder *Alnus glutinosa*, gorse *Ulex europeaeus* and red clover *Trifolium pratense*.

❑ Which of these three species would you expect to be most suitable as nitrogen fixers in china clay waste tips?

■ *Alnus* is a species found in wet habitats; even in Cornwall, the tips are likely to dry out in summer because of their low water-holding capacity. Red clover, a herbaceous species of agricultural land, might be successful, but is likely to be affected by the relatively low pH levels of the tips. Gorse is typically a species of acid heaths and so is the most likely candidate.

In practice, one of the most effective species for revegetation of these tips has proved to be the tree lupin *Lupinus arboreus*. Figure 3.18 shows the effect of *Lupinus* on the surrounding vegetation over a period of six years after seeding with lupin.

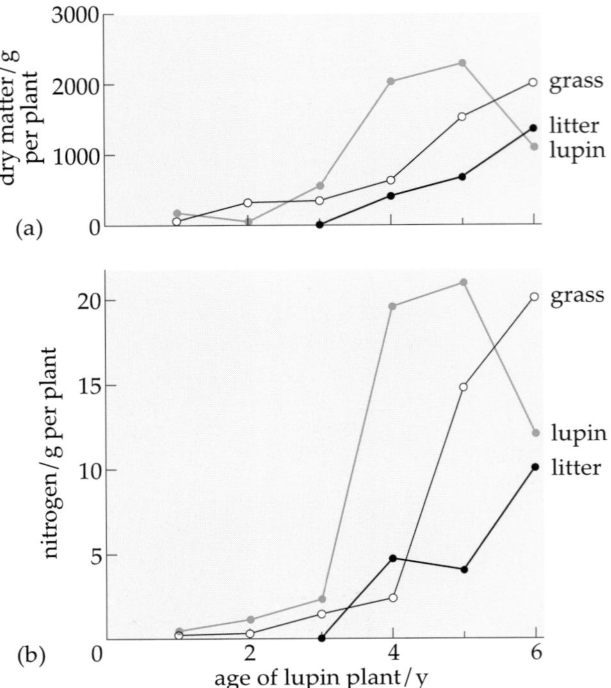

Figure 3.18 The effect of *Lupinus arboreus* on surrounding vegetation growing on china clay waste. Vegetation is measured as (a) dry matter, g per plant, and (b) nitrogen, g per plant. In the absence of the lupin, there is no grass growth.

Fixation rates up to 150 kg of nitrogen per hectare per annum have been reported for *Lupinus* in New Zealand. A secondary advantage of legumes is that the litter which they deposit also mineralizes more rapidly than does the litter from non-legumes. The vegetation in a poorly productive temperate ecosystem takes up about 100 kg N ha^{-1} y^{-1} and a productive ecosystem takes up twice as much. About 1/16th of the organic nitrogen in a cool temperate soil is mineralized per annum.

❑ What size of organic nitrogen pool would be needed to maintain a productive ecosystem on china clay spoil?

■ $200 \times 16 = 3200$ kg of nitrogen per hectare.

❑ How long would it take to establish a pool of this size, relying on nitrogen fixation by *Lupinus*?

■ 3200/150, i.e. 20 years at least.

In many cases, such a slow rate of accumulation (and the calculation assumed a high rate of fixation) would be unacceptable, so the first stage of revegetation requires fertilizer applications to raise the initial capital of nitrogen present.

Summary of Section 3.4

- There is a large area of land which is classified as derelict, a state resulting from previous human activity.
- Absence of vegetation, or inappropriate vegetation on such sites, may result from a range of physical and biological limitations.
- Various civil and biological engineering techniques exist to remediate derelict land.
- Shortage of nutrients and excess of toxic materials are very common causes of dereliction.
- Experimental methods are needed to identify the factors limiting vegetation on derelict land and to suggest appropriate techniques for revegetation.

Question 3.5

(Objective 3.7)

'Red mud' is the major waste from aluminium oxide extraction from bauxite ore. In the USA, some 10×10^6 t are produced annually and stored in ponds. The red mud has a pH value of between 9.0 and 12.5, and a high content of soluble aluminium and sodium. It forms a poorly drained, anaerobic medium, which supports no vegetation. Desert saltgrass *Distichles spiralis* has been observed to grow in soils with pH values up to 10.7. It is a rhizomatous perennial, but rarely produces seeds. The rhizomes possess aerenchyma, so it can grow in anaerobic soils.

In a series of experiments, desert saltgrass was grown in pots of red mud, either alone, or with various 'amendments' added to the red mud, with or without additional nutrients. As a control, plants were grown in sand, with a complete nutrient solution. Figure 3.19 shows the response of the saltgrass to these amendments.

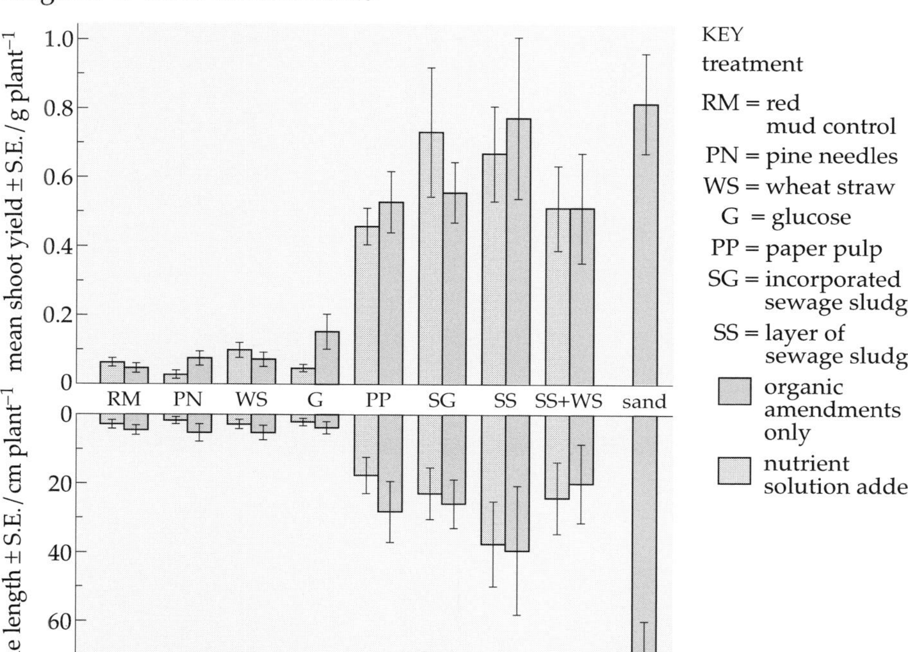

Figure 3.19 Mean shoot yields and mean rhizome lengths of desert saltgrass shoots after $4\frac{1}{2}$ months in red mud with organic amendments alone (coloured bars) and with a nutrient solution addition (shaded bars). Rhizome growth in the SS (sewage sludge layer) and SS + WS treatments occurred only below the layer of sludge.

(a) From the data provided, suggest what factor in the unameliorated mud prevents plant growth.

(b) Suggest a practical way of vegetating red mud lagoons.

(c) What would limit the applicability of your suggestions?

Question 3.6

(Objective 3.7)

Thlaspi caerulescens is a hyperaccumulator of zinc and cadmium, and can exhibit concentrations as high as 20 000 and 160 mg of the two metals respectively per kg of shoot biomass. In an experiment to test the usefulness of this species for reclamation of contaminated soils, *Thlaspi* plants and tomato plants (*Lycopersicon esculenta*) were grown in pots filled with three contaminated soils from near a zinc smelter. The pH of the soils was adjusted to three different levels. Characteristics of the soil in the different treatments and the amounts of zinc and cadmium in the shoots of the plants were as shown in Table 3.9. Figure 3.20 shows the dry weight yield of shoot tissue in the different treatments.

Table 3.9 Characteristics of the contaminated soils and total amounts of heavy metal in shoots of *Thlaspi caerulescens* and *Lycopersicon esculenta* grown in pots in those soils. (Data from Brown *et al.*, 1994.)

Site	pH	Soil		*Thlaspi*		Tomato	
		Zn/mg kg^{-1}	Cd/mg kg^{-1}	Zn/mg pot^{-1}	Cd/μg pot^{-1}	Zn/mg pot^{-1}	Cd/μg pot^{-1}
	5.06			3.05	250	0.4	6.6
1	5.81	2100	38	16.0	504	1.2	30.5
	6.82			20.5	186	0.9	38.3
	5.07			8.5	117	0.6	3
2	5.42	4100	38	29.4	571	0.3	1
	6.37			12.7	765	0.4	2.4
	5.84			11.5	389	0.3	4.5
3	6.67	48 000	1020	66.2	3650	0.3	1.8
	7.04			36	4131	0.3	6.6

(a) Summarize the results of the experiment.

(b) Do the results suggest that *Thlaspi* could be used for reducing the levels of contaminant in these soils?

(c) From earlier information given in this Book, suggest one other role for this species in dealing with contaminated materials.

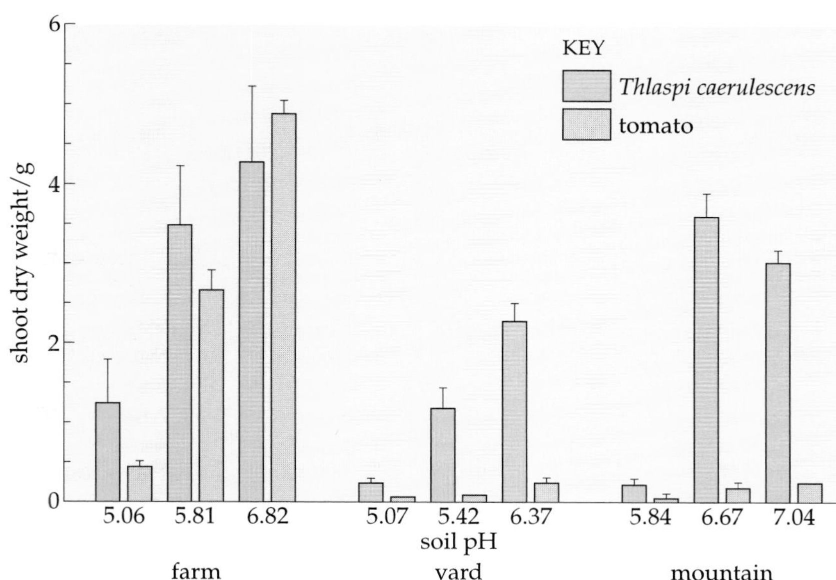

Figure 3.20 Dry weight yield of stem tissue for *Thlaspi* and tomato plants grown in the three different soils.

3.5 Conservation of habitats and species

In Section 2.5, destruction of habitats was identified as one factor leading to loss of species. The data in Section 1.2 on the use of arable set-aside by birds suggested that a number of previously declining species benefited from the absence of normal agricultural operations. So one possible way of conserving species in the UK might be to abandon existing agricultural management and allow land to revert to a more natural condition.

3.5.1 The importance of historic systems of land use

The Geescroft wilderness experiment at the Rothamsted Experimental Station in Hertfordshire may indicate some of the possible longer term effects of set-aside. Agricultural experiments have been conducted at Rothamsted since the mid-19th century and two areas were deliberately set aside in the mid-1880s as **wildernesses**, with no further agricultural activity imposed upon them.

The site lies on a gently undulating plateau of clay-with-flints overlying chalk at about 130 m above sea-level, north of London. It had a long history of cultivation, being recorded in 1623 as arable land. Tile-drains were laid in the soil in 1849, and the area formed part of an experiment growing beans with or without phosphate fertilizers from 1842 until 1878. The bean crops were increasingly infested with weeds, and there were numerous crop failures towards the end of the period. From 1878 to 1882, it was 'bare fallowed' (i.e. cultivated but not sown), and then a clover crop was sown in 1883. It was fenced off in 1886 and then left alone. Botanical surveys were taken in 1867, 1903, 1913, 1957 and 1983, and light traps for insect sampling were installed in 1947. Some dying elms were felled, and a standing ash tree stolen (!) in 1977. In 1957 and 1983, detailed numerical surveys of species were made, as far as possible using the transects set up in 1913. Some species which no longer occurred on the transects were noted elsewhere in the wilderness. Results of the botanical surveys are given in Table 3.10 using a Domin scale. Figure 3.21 shows views of the wilderness in 1938 and 1957. Study the Table, and then attempt the questions which follow.

Table 3.10 The variation in the flora of the Geescroft wilderness area from 1867 to 1983. Species are divided into six broad categories, and into six levels of relative abundance, A–X. Data are number of species in each category. (Data derived from Brenchly and Adam, 1915.)

Species category	Abundance	1867	1903	1913	1957	1983
small grasses	A			2		
Poa annua, Briza media, Festuca ovina, Cynosurus cristatus, etc.	C			2		
	F	2		1		
	O		2	2		
	R		1		1	
	X					
large grasses, sedges, other monocotyledons	A		1	1	1	
Deschampsia cespitosa, Arrhenatherum elatius, Holcus Lanatus	C		2		3	
Arum maculatum, Hyacinthoides non-scriptus, etc.	F	4		6		1
	O		4	8	2	1
	R		2		6	2
	X					1
dicotyledonous arable weeds	A				1	
Ranunculus acris, Papaver rhoeas, Urtica dioica, Rumex	C			2	1	
obtusifolius, etc.	F	40		1	1	
	O		5	12		1
	R				3	
	X					3
other herbaceous dicotyledons	A				2	
Viola odorata, Anthriscus sylvestris, Heracleum sphondylium	C		1	1	1	
Centaurea nigra, etc.	F			1		
	O		5	35	1	2
	R		2		8	
	X					3

ferns	A					
Dryopteris filix-mas, Ophioglossum vulgatum, Pteridium aquilinum	C					
	F					
	O			3		
	R				1	
	X					1
shrubs and trees	A				2	
Crataegus monogyna, Quercus robur, Acer campestre, Ilex aquifolium, Ribes sylvestre, etc.	C				1	3
	F				2	1
	O				6	4
	R				4	5
	X			9		4
total no. of species:						
present on transect		46	25	77	40	20
(in whole wood area)				(86)		(32)
Shannon index, *H*					4.38	3.66

Key: A = Abundant, C = Common, F = Frequent, O = Occasional, R = Rare, X = Recorded in wood, but not on transect.

(a)

(b)

Figure 3.21 Geescroft wilderness at two dates in its development (a) 1938; (b) 1957.

❑ What are the major changes in flora that have occurred in the Geescroft wilderness?

■ The obvious major change is in number of species present. The actual species present in 1867 were mainly weeds typical of a badly maintained garden, which were replaced by other dicotyledonous herbs and by grasses over the period to 1913. By 1957, tree and shrub species had become the major component of the vegetation.

❑ At which date was the diversity of the flora highest?

■ This cannot be answered directly, since we need comparable quantitative data from each sampling date to make such a comparison. The total number of species recorded fell from 46 during the period of arable cultivation to 25, rose to a peak in 1913, then declined to 1983.

❑ Table 3.10 gives the values of H, the Shannon index of diversity (see Section 1.2 and Book 2, Chapters 2 and 3) for the data in 1957 and 1983. Comment on these two values in this context.

■ As would be expected from the larger number of species recorded on the transects in 1957 (47 compared to 20), the index of diversity H was higher then than in 1983. Another aspect of diversity is the equitability or evenness, E which is calculated by H/H_{max} (H_{max} the maximum value of H that could be found with that number of species). The values of E are 0.79 for 1957 and 0.84 for 1983. H_{max} values (i.e. $\log_2 S$) would be 5.55 and 4.32 respectively. Thus, although total diversity fell between 1957 and 1983, equitability increased slightly. This presumably reflects the disappearance by 1983 of the species on the transects which were only present in very small numbers in 1957, and a general evening out of numbers among the surviving species.

The change in flora of Geescroft shows, as you might expect, a reversion to what is regarded as the natural flora of this part of the UK – woodland. However, the woodland flora was much less diverse than that of the original arable field, so abandoning agricultural activity may not lead to the recreation of a species-rich natural community.

❑ Suggest why there is this decrease in diversity in the Geescroft data.

■ A major reason is that the starting point is not late 20th century agriculture but that of the 19th century, where weed control depended almost entirely on cultivation and sequencing of crops (rotation) rather than on species-selective herbicides and so a much more diverse flora was originally present compared to the later years.

The Geescroft study shows the possible results of a passive policy for conservation. The wilderness may well be 'natural', but its current flora is remarkably impoverished. Nearby woodlands that have never been clear-felled contain many more species, including bluebell (*Hyacinthoides non-scriptus*), dog's mercury (*Mercurialis perennis*), primrose (*Primula vulgaris*), wood anemone (*anemone nemoralis*), wood sorrel (*Oxalis acetosella*), wood millet (*Milium effusum*) and the rarer wild daffodil (*Narcissus pseudo-narcissus*). Of these, only *Hyacinthoides* and *Mercurialis* are found in Geescroft; the distribution of *Mercurialis* between 1973 and 1974 was reported by Pigott (1977) and is shown in Figure 3.22.

❑ Why might *M. perennis* have the distribution shown in Figure 3.22? Why should the majority of the species listed above be absent from the Geescroft flora in 1983?

- *M. perennis* is only found near the edges of the wilderness; this is almost certainly due to its spreading from the surrounding, managed, hedges. There are several possible explanations for the absence of species in 1983. There may be some barrier to their dispersal, so they are unable to reach the woodland. Soil conditions may differ between Geescroft and elsewhere. Another explanation is that they only enter the woodland once it reaches a greater degree of heterogeneity; at present, the stand of trees is relatively even-aged.

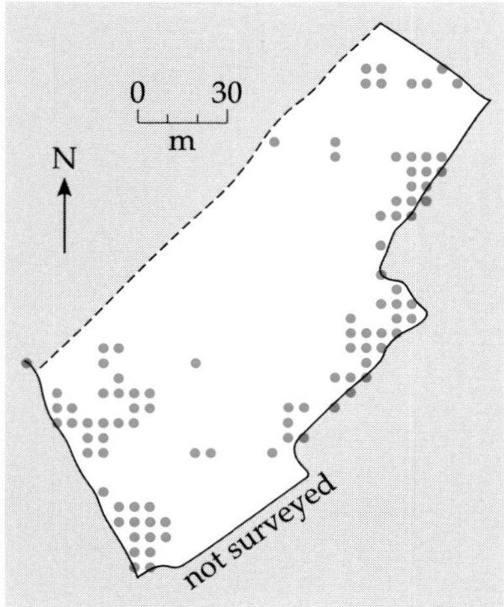

Figure 3.22 Distribution of *Mercurialis perennis* (green dots) in Geescroft wilderness, based on a survey in 1973–74. Solid lines are old hedgerows and the broken line is a fence separating the wilderness from the adjacent field. The south-eastern extremity is influenced by the adjacent road and was not surveyed.

Although the more species-rich ancient woodlands have not been clear felled, they are not 'untouched by human hand'. The understorey was usually managed by coppicing, i.e. cutting at intervals of 7–14 years to provide firewood and raw material (see also Book 3, Chapter 1). **Coppicing** reduced the understorey shade, and the regular trampling also assisted in maintaining a pre-climax community. To conserve such communities requires *active* landscape management, but many historic management practices are no longer economic or even relevant. The split-hazel washing basket of 50 years ago has long since given way to plastic. Wattle hurdles have been replaced by their tubular metal equivalents, and the demand for hurdles has decreased as it is no longer economic to **fold** (i.e. to graze in hurdled enclosures) sheep on root crops. In small areas, it may be feasible to reproduce coppice management, but this is not economically viable on a larger scale. Conditions may change; in 1996, there were proposals for the introduction of 'short rotation coppice' using willow, poplar and other fast growing species, as a source of wood chip to fuel an electricity generation plant in Eastern England. However, largely monospecific stands of these species may not carry a very diverse flora either.

3.5.2 Butterfly conservation

One of the habitat types in Britain which has declined most dramatically in extent over the last 50 years is species-rich grassland. This has either been ploughed and converted to arable, or has received increased applications of fertilizer, which has changed the balance of species in favour of the faster-growing grasses such as ryegrass *Lolium perenne*. The responsive species have a high **nitrogen score** (defined in the TV programme 'The Big Picture'). In the 1960s, identifying the processes which caused 'deterioration' of pure swards of *Lolium* (i.e. mainly ingress of species such as *Poa annua* and *Agrostis* spp.) was a major focus of agricultural research. In terms of agricultural production, this made sense, although at the time there was also a significant volume of literature which suggested that the production per unit of fertilizer input of these so-called secondary grasses often equalled, and in particular conditions could exceed, that of ryegrass.

In the UK, species-rich chalk grassland represents an early successional stage, and, like coppiced woodland, is an important habitat for a number of species which are highly valued by humans for their 'aesthetic' qualities. Examples of this include several butterflies and some of these are shown on p. 122–3 – the Adonis blue, *Lysandra bellargus*, (Rott), the silver spotted skipper, *Hesperia comma* (L.) and the silver studded blue *Plebejus argus* (L.), are threatened with extinction in the UK. The story of the now extinct large blue, *Maculinea arion* (L), was examined in Chapter 1, Book 1, and showed how this was dependent on the existence of a sufficient area of early successional communities in its habitat.

❑ Is it likely that these early successional communities would reappear on set-aside land?

■ Although set-aside is, by definition, an early successional stage, the starting point is very different from any 'natural' situation. The total pool of available nutrients in the soil is high as a result of previous fertilizer use, and this favours the coarser-growing grasses for a prolonged period. Another factor in maintaining species-rich grassland is grazing, and in 1995 legislation precluded grazing of agricultural livestock (which excluded horses) on set-aside land except where this formed part of Environmentally Sensitive Area (ESA) legislation.

The grazing experiment discussed in Book 2, Chapter 3, showed the resistance to species ingress exhibited by agricultural grassland. One way of overcoming the problem of the high nutrient content of ex-agricultural soils is actually to strip off the topsoil, an activity which is hardly consistant with popular ideas of 'conservation'. However, there are circumstances such as road building where earthmoving operations are inevitable, and these could offer an opportunity for recreating the habitat for particular species. Morris *et al.* (1994) described an example of one attempt to do this.

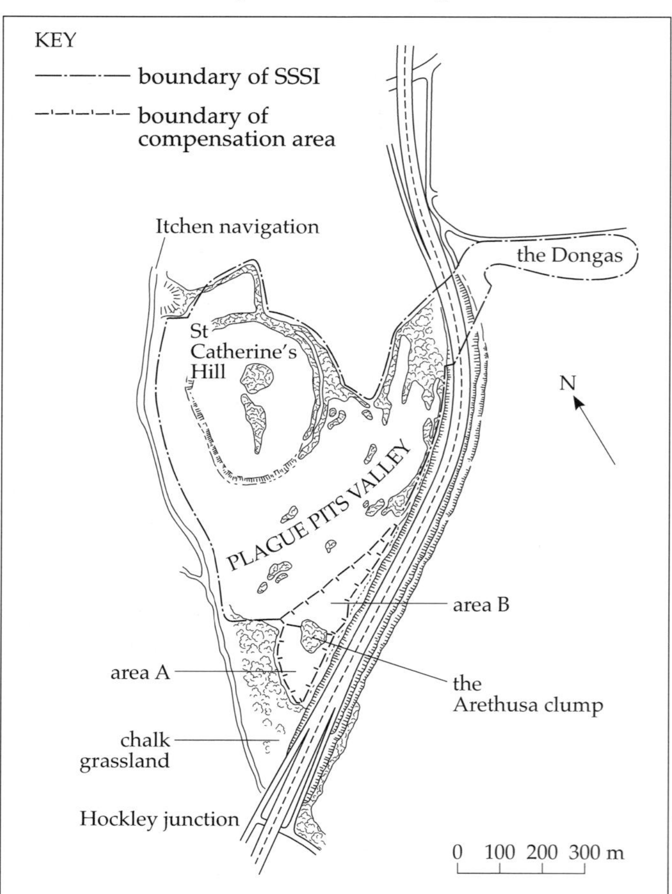

Figure 3.23 Location of the St Catherine's Hill SSSI and the 'compensation area' allocated in exchange.

Construction of a section of the London–Southampton motorway would destroy a section of a Site of Special Scientific Interest, and plans included the establishment of a '**compensation area**' as shown in Figure 3.23. The objectives for the work on this compensation area were to re-establish species-rich grassland 'characteristic of that part of the Hampshire chalk' (Calcicolous Grassland 2 of the National Vegetation Classification) and to encourage several species of uncommon butterflies and insects.

The area of the original SSSI called the Dongas had been neglected over the years, and carried species-rich grassland, species-poor grassland and scrubland. Table 3.11 gives the characteristics of the soils on areas of the Dongas carrying these different vegetation types, and on the compensation area.

Table 3.11 Soil characteristics of the compensation site and three areas of the Dongas carrying different vegetation types. Asterisks denote significant differences between the compensation site and the Dongas site (*= $p < 0.05$; **= $p < 0.005$; ***= $p < 0.001$; no data = n.d.).

Variable	Compensation		Dongas	
	site	species-rich	species-poor	scrub
pH	7.88	7.88	7.73 **	7.61***
% loss on ignition	13.07	13.55	20.16*	25.07**
total nitrogen/mg 100 g^{-1} soil	0.51	0.46	0.95	1.08***
phosphate/mg 100 g^{-1} soil	2.69	1.32**	1.47*	1.72**
magnesium/mg 100 g^{-1} soil	7.21	7.57	16.32*	29.69**
calcium/mg 100 g^{-1} soil	836.7	516.2	856.0	1081
potassium/mg 100 g^{-1} soil	10.18	18.49**	9.76	13.82
clay (%)	43.58	n.d.	89.43**	80.20*
silt (%)	23.89	n.d.	14.89**	16.39*

❑ Are the data in Table 3.11 consistent with the suggestion that low levels of plant nutrients in the soil are an essential prerequisite for species-rich grassland?

■ Not entirely. Within the Dongas site, nutrient levels are generally higher in the species-poor and scrub areas than in the species-rich area, except for potassium which is highest in the species-rich area.

❑ How closely do the data for the compensation area match those for species-rich grassland, and what is the major difference?

■ The nutrient levels and pH in the compensation area soil are generally similar to those in the species-rich area, with the exception of phosphate, which is higher, and potassium, which is lower.

The data suggest that, with the exception of phosphate, which could pose a problem, soil conditions on the compensation site were appropriate for the re-creation of species-rich grassland. The Dongas site would provide both seed and turf for this process, and a list of species was drawn up that was to be seeded or planted into the compensation site. A major aspect of the project was to favour rarer butterflies and insects, and some of these, particularly those associated with ant hills, had very specific temperature and humidity requirements. Figure 3.24 overleaf shows a temperature profile across a *Lasius flavus* (ant) mound, with a 6 to 10° C variation along the north–south and east–west axes. Eight butterfly species which could breed in the area were identified (see margins) and the microhabitats of these relative to ant-mound topography are shown in Figure 3.25.

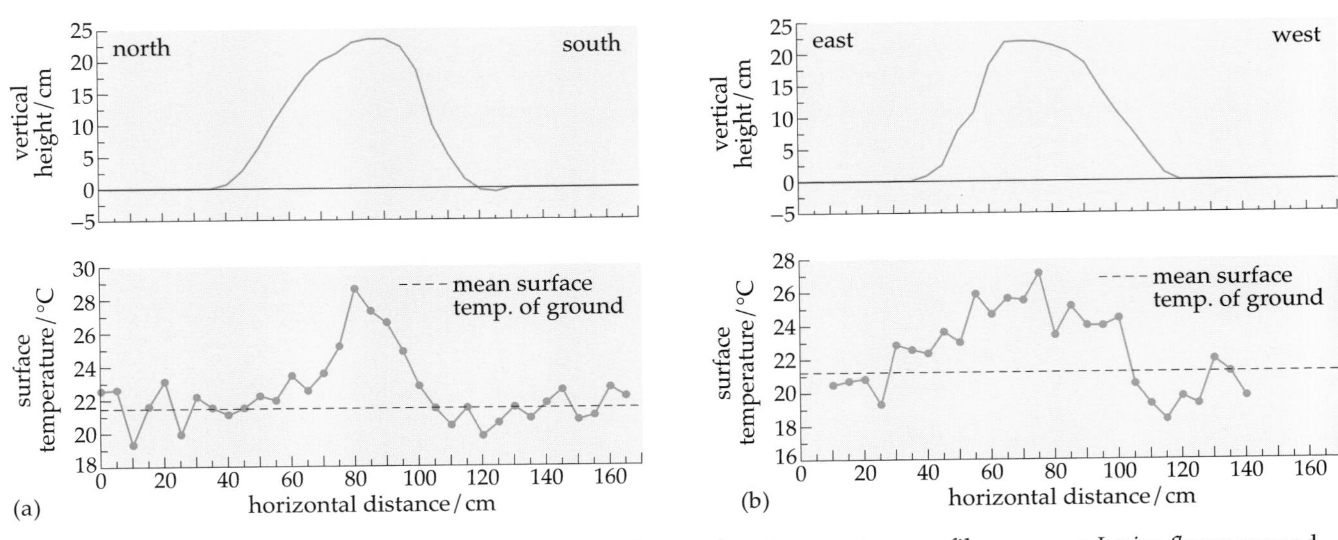

Figure 3.24 September surface temperature profiles across a *Lasius flavus* mound for (a) north-south and (b) east-west axes.

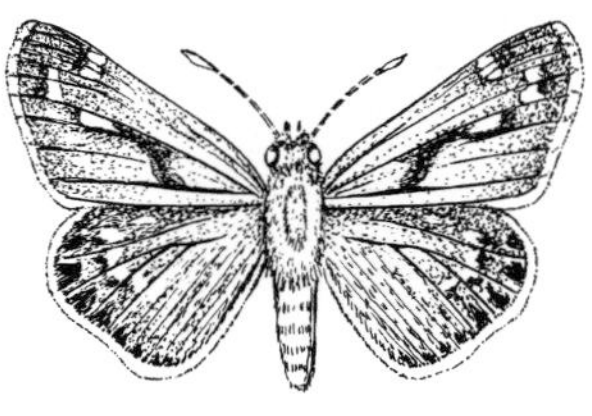

Hesperia comma
(× 1.25)

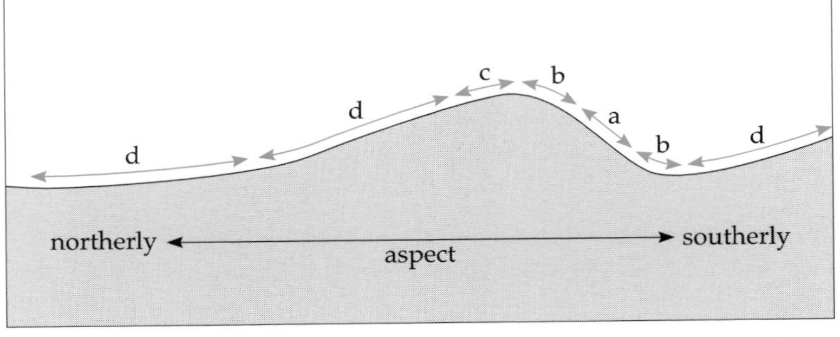

Figure 3.25 Distribution of microhabitats of the eight rarest species of butterflies that could breed on the site; a = very sparse, warm turf with much bare chalk (*H. comma, H. semele, C. minimus*); b = sparse, dry warm turf (*L. bellargus, L. coridon, A. agestis, C. minimus*); c = short, well-drained turf (*L. coridon, A. agestis, C. minimus*); d = cooler, deeper turf (*H. lucina, A. aglaja*).

Argynnis aglaja
(× 0.6)

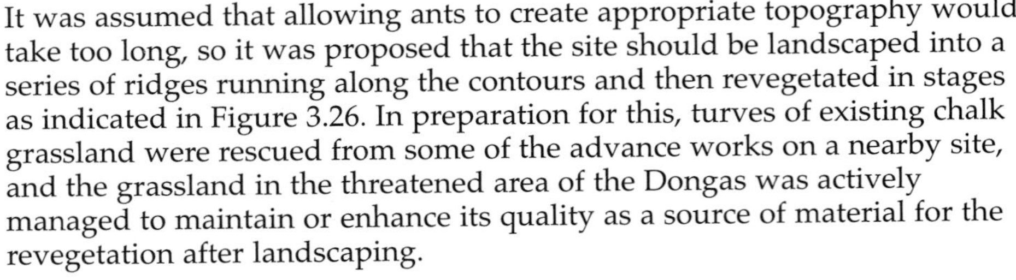

It was assumed that allowing ants to create appropriate topography would take too long, so it was proposed that the site should be landscaped into a series of ridges running along the contours and then revegetated in stages as indicated in Figure 3.26. In preparation for this, turves of existing chalk grassland were rescued from some of the advance works on a nearby site, and the grassland in the threatened area of the Dongas was actively managed to maintain or enhance its quality as a source of material for the revegetation after landscaping.

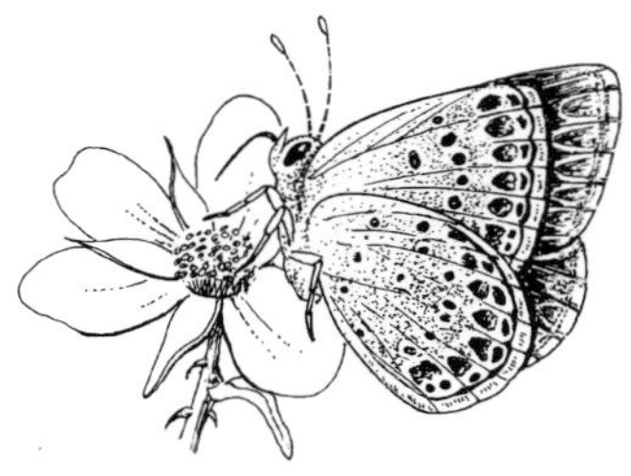

Aricia agestis
(× 1.75)

The plan outlined here indicates that conservation of rare species or recreation of habitats in a country such as the UK may need intensive human intervention, based on detailed understanding of the dynamics of the vegetation, the requirements of the species which are to be protected and of the relationships between these and small-scale landform. In

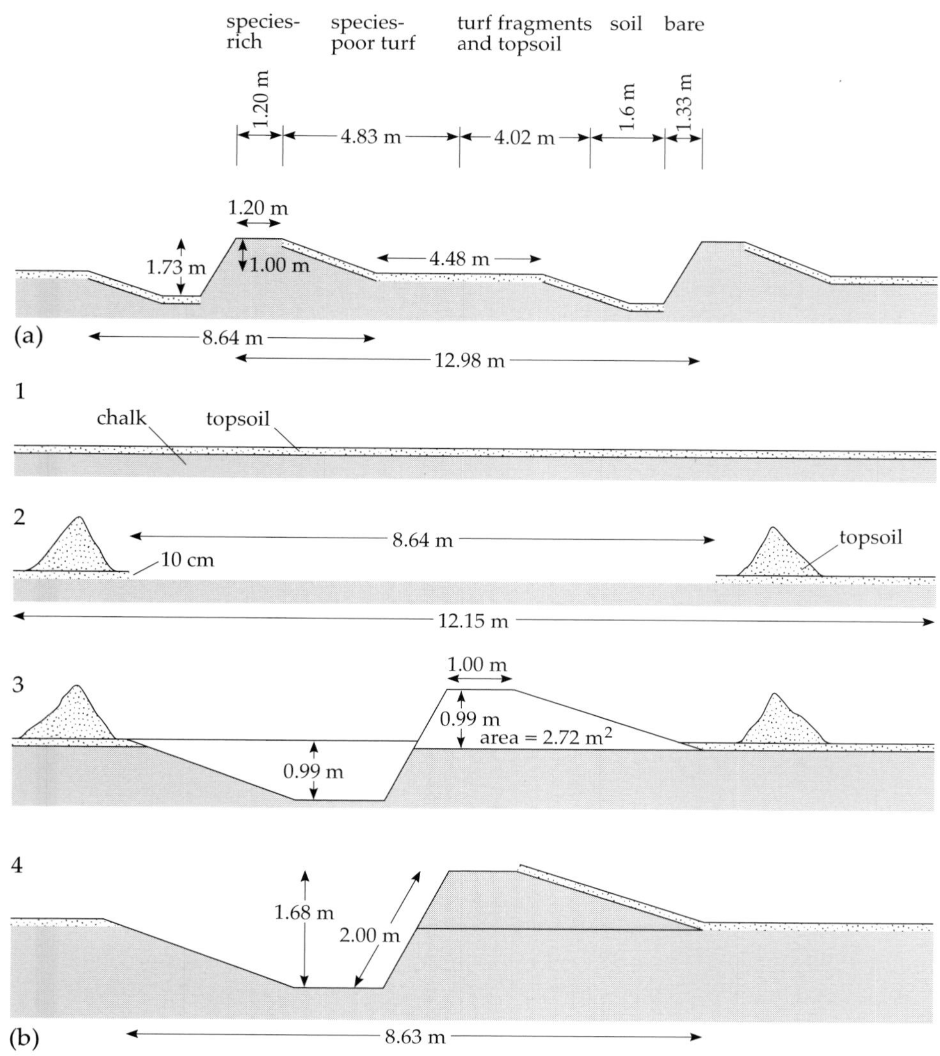

Figure 3.26 (a) Final section and origin of surface-covering materials, and (b) proposed method of constructing the ridges to provide microhabitats for butterflies in the compensation area.

Hipparchia semele (× 1.0)

Hamearis lucina (× 1.0)

Lysandra bellargus (× 1.25)

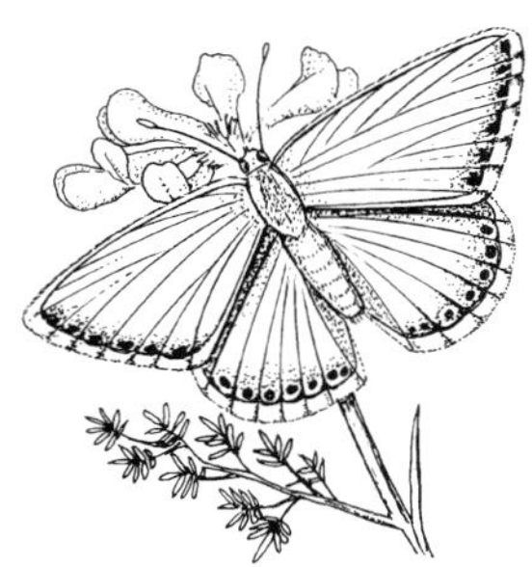

Lysandra coridon (× 1.25)

Cupido minimus (× 1.0)

addition, care has to be taken over selection of propagules (to ensure that these are relevant **ecotypes**, if this is important), rather than just using whatever is available.

It is salutary, however, to note the conclusion of this story. In the end, the proposals for landscaping and revegtation were rejected, for two main reasons:

(i) The area was part of a Scheduled Ancient Monument, and archaeologists were understandably reluctant to support the proposed earthmoving activities.

(ii) Perhaps less understandably, there was opposition from local conservation and amenity groups who were concerned about the visual impact of the scheme.

Pity the poor ecologist.

Summary of Section 3.5

- Human activity has often been associated with the loss of desired habitats and communities.
- Removal of human management from an area may not result in the re-creation of the valued pre-existing habitat.
- Re-creation of desired habitats and communities requires detailed knowledge of the ecology of those communities.
- Many valued species-rich communities are the result of human activity in earlier periods, activity which currently is not economically viable.
- There is potential conflict between different aspects of conservation.

Question 3.7

(Objective 3.5)

'Herb-rich grassland' is a feature of the Yorkshire Dales area of the UK, mentioned in the TV programme 'The Big Picture'. It is grazed by sheep and cattle, and cut for hay each year. To maintain the floristic richness of this grassland, it is necessary to restrict fertilizer application, and to cut for hay in July or August. During 1987 to 1991, trials of different grazing regimes were carried out on grassland cut for hay. Treatments were:

(i) no grazing at any time of the year;

(ii) grazing with sheep only from January to May;

(iii) grazing in September–October with cattle only and then with sheep only to December;

(iv) 'normal grazing', i.e. the grazing treatments in (ii) and (iii) combined.

Table 3.12 shows the species richness, species diversity and total biomass at the time of hay cropping for the four treatments in 1991.

Table 3.12 Species richness, diversity and biomass (g m^{-2}) under four grazing treatments on hay meadows in the Yorkshire Dales. Values in any row without common superscripts differ significantly $p < 0.05$. (Data from Smith and Rushton, 1994.)

	Treatment			
	(i)	**(ii)**	**(iii)**	**(iv)**
species richness	15.6^{b}	18.8^{a}	19.0^{a}	20.9^{a}
species diversity	$9.2b^{c}$	10.5^{ab}	10.3^{ac}	11.6^{a}
biomass	47.8^{c}	31.2^{ab}	39.0^{bc}	26.4^{a}

(a) Summarize the effects of the different grazing regimes.

(b) What do the data in the Table indicate about the importance of the traditional grazing regime in maintaining floristic diversity?

Question 3.8

(Objectives 3.5 & 3.7)

In north-western Europe, the area of *Calluna*-dominated heathland has declined dramatically as former heathland has been converted to arable. With the reduction in arable agriculture required by set-aside regulation in the 1990s, experiments were set up to examine the possibility of recreating

Calluna heathland on arable land. Table 3.13 shows some characteristics of soil from existing *Calluna* heathland, from uncultivated arable soil and from the remaining arable soil after 300–400 mm had been removed from its surface. Figure 3.27 shows the extractable nitrogen and phosphorus from the same soils over a one-year period.

(a) What are the distinctive features of the *Calluna* heathland soil?

(b) Would removal of the top 300–400 mm of the arable soil be an advantage in trying to recreate *Calluna* heathland?

(c) What other activities would be necessary to recreate *Calluna* heathland in this area?

Table 3.13 Characteristics of soil from a *Calluna* heath (CH), nearby uncultivated arable (UA), and arable soil from which the topsoil had been removed (SA). (Data from Aerts *et al.*, 1995.)

Soil characteristic		**CH**	**UA**	**SA**
organic matter	$/\text{mg g}^{-1}$	60.9[a]	77.5[b]	11.1[c]
total carbon		29.4[a]	43.0[b]	4.1[c]
total nitrogen		0.87[a]	1.18[b]	0.15[c]
total phosphorus		0.026[a]	1.613[b]	0.013[a]
C/N ratio		34.6[a]	36.8[a]	28.9[a]
C/P ratio		1190.0[a]	28.1[b]	334.2[c]
Calluna seed	(viable buried seed m^{-2})	26500[a]	0[b]	0[b]
forb seed		5200[a]	7600[a]	2400[b]
grass seed		600[a]	2900[b]	300[a]

Values in each row with different superscripts differ significantly, $P < 0.05$.

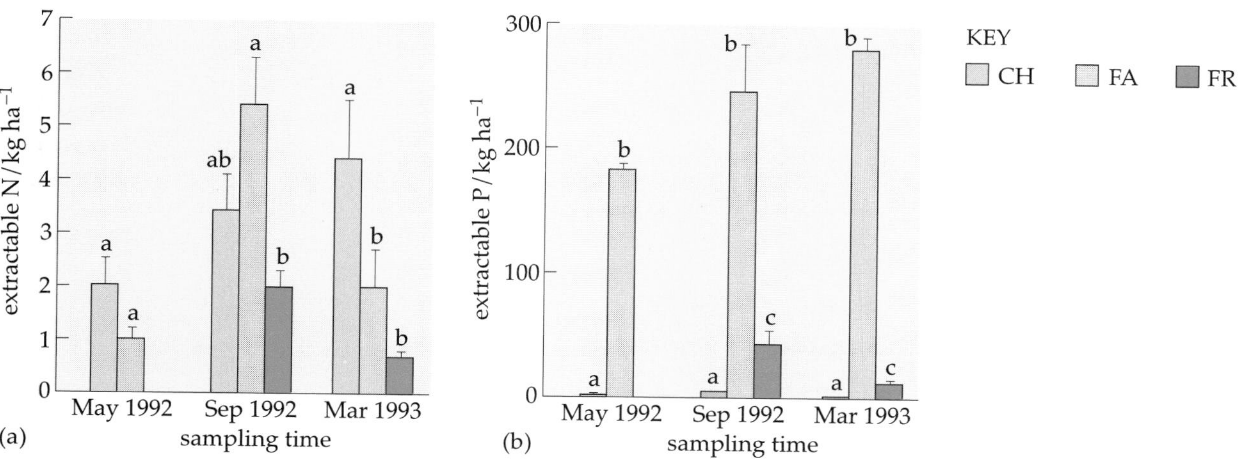

Figure 3.27 Extractable nitrogen (a) and phosphorus (b) from the three soils over a one-year period.

3.6 Release of genetically modified organisms

In Section 2.5.2, we considered the ecological effects of transgenic organisms. Deciding when and how such organisms may be released requires that the potential environmental impact of the release be considered, and this is at least as complex as other examples mentioned earlier.

Considerable effort has been devoted to the development of **biocontrol agents**, including **biopesticides** which are toxic compounds derived from bacteria or fungi, and used to control particular pests. Toxins from *Bacillus thuringiensis* have been the major example, with a potential market estimated at $60m. The genes for these toxins can be inserted into other organisms with the aim of providing protection against insect pests.

❑ What effect might such genetically engineered species have on other species in the field?

■ Almost any result could occur, but if the genetically engineered organism was more competitive than organisms with a similar niche in the field, the introduced organism could replace wild species.

More subtle effects could also occur. Many of the organisms currently being investigated are bacteria since they are easier to manipulate and to culture than are higher organisms. However, transfer of genetic material between species occurs more readily among microorganisms. The genes used to make a particular organism into an effective control agent for a pest could be transferred to another organism and enable it to become pathogenic to some other species.

Table 3.14 shows the frequency of transfer of genetic material between two bacterial species when incubated in sterilized or unsterilized soil, alone or with additions of bentonite (a clay mineral which provides attachment sites for the bacteria) and of microbial nutrients.

Table 3.14 Frequency of transfer of genetic material (transfers per 10^7 cells) between *Bacillus cereus* and *B. subtilis* in soil over a two-day period. (Data from van Elsas *et al.*, 1987.)

Treatment	Transfers
unsterilized soil	0
unsterilized soil + bentonite	0.8
sterilized soil	0
sterilized soil + nutrients	0.5
sterilized soil + nutrients + bentonite	5

Table 3.14 suggests that the presence of microsites, and of conditions for rapid microbial growth, favour the transfer of genetic material, but clearly, transfer of genetic material can take place in the field.

The complexity of the issues surrounding the development and release of transgenic organisms is indicated by the **baculoviruses**. These only infect invertebrates, primarily plant-feeding larval stages of Lepidoptera. The viruses only multiply within plant-feeding species; some are highly host-specific, whereas others can infect a wider range of lepidopteran species.

The baculovirus is picked up from the foliage of the food plant, and multiplies within the body of the host, ultimately almost always killing it, and leaving the skin as a sac of **virus occlusion bodies** (the virus plus a protective protein coat). When the skin sac decomposes, the occlusion bodies are released to infect other susceptible larvae. The protective protein coat of the occlusion bodies allows the baculovirus to persist under appropriate conditions for a long period, although they are rapidly inactivated by ultraviolet radiation. This combination of specificity, high pathogenicity and the fact that they are readily destroyed by UV but can be stored, makes them excellent candidates for biopesticides.

The disadvantage of baculoviruses is that during the period that they are replicating within the host, the host is still causing damage to the crop plant. In contrast, most synthesized pesticides give rapid **knock down** and so provide a greater yield benefit, but this is at the expense of their possible side-effects on other organisms.

Virus particles can be modified by the use of **recombinant DNA technology**, to increase their speed of action. Investigators at the NERC Institute of Virology and Environmental Microbiology in Oxford and other research centres world-wide have been examining a range of genes that could be inserted into the baculoviruses for this purpose. Candidate genes included those for insect-selective toxins and insect hormones and enzymes. The most effective was that for an insect-selective toxin produced by the North African scorpion *Androctonus australis*. In the laboratory, the modified baculovirus killed caterpillars of susceptible species in only 75% of the time taken by the unmodified virus. To test whether this would translate into effective control in the field, it was necessary to undertake field trials, and in the UK these can only be undertaken with the permission of the Advisory Committee on Release to the Environment (ACRE) formerly the Genetic Manipulation Advisory Group. This group required an appropriate **risk analysis** of the **probabilities** of the engineered organism causing damage in the environment. The conditions proposed for the tests included the use of insect-proof cages each of 1 m^3, in which cabbage plants were grown and infected with cabbage looper (*Trichoplusia ni*) larvae. They were sprayed with either the normal or the genetically modified baculovirus and the damage to the cabbage was assessed in terms of the amount of leaf area eaten. Figure 3.28 shows the results of the assessment.

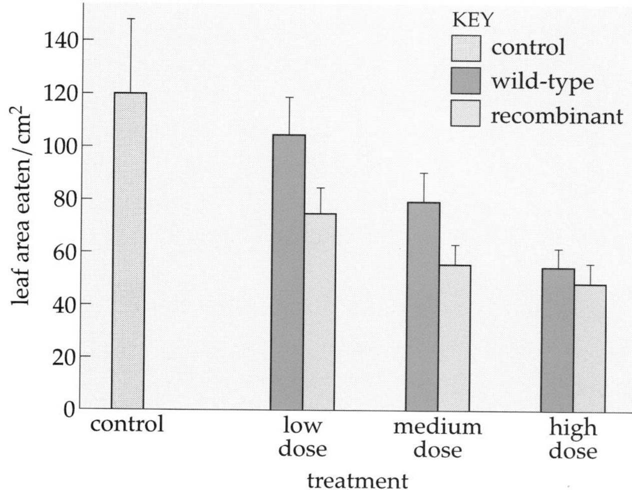

Figure 3.28 Damage to cabbage plants in untreated cages, and in those treated with low, medium and high doses of normal and engineered baculovirus.

❑ What was the effect of the two baculovirus types on the amount of damage?

■ Treatment with either type of baculovirus reduced damage at all the application rates with the exception of the low rate application/normal baculovirus combination where damage was reduced, but not significantly. At low and medium application rates, less damage was recorded when the engineered baculovirus rather than the normal type baculovirus was used.

Figure 3.29 suggests that the engineered baculovirus was a more effective control measure for the cabbage looper than was the normal type, since it was effective at lower doses. The second aspect which needed investigation was the persistence of the baculovirus. A number of factors influence this. It was found that larvae attacked by the engineered virus produced fewer occlusion bodies per cadaver. Since the scorpion toxin also paralysed them they did not exhibit the same behaviour as those infected with the normal type. The behaviour changes resulted in fewer virus particles being released after the death of the host. This reduced the effectiveness of the baculovirus as an insecticide, but also reduced the chances of its infecting other, non-target organisms.

As a test of the baculovirus, the experiments were a success. However, as a public relations exercise, it was perhaps unwise to have undertaken this first release of a genetically engineered baculovirus on the edge of Wytham Wood, with its long history of ecological studies. Some scientists regarded the possibility of vandal damage to the cages (which were lightweight timber constructions) to pose an unacceptable risk – the modified virus could be released to infect other lepidopteran species, with unknown results. At the time of writing (1995), this controversy is still rumbling on, and permission for further studies in the field is being withheld.

Summary of Section 3.6

- Genetic manipulation allows the production of novel biological entities which can be used as pesticides or for other biocontrol purposes.
- The potential ecological effects of the use of transgenic organisms in the field are not fully known, but the organisms are supposedly designed to minimize environmental impact.
- Exchange of genetic material between microorganisms could cause significant changes in naturally occurring organisms and with unknown consequences.
- Use of biopesticides is limited by their relative slowness of action, and genetic engineering to improve this aspect may affect the interactions of the biopesticide with other non-target species.
- Experimental examination of the effects of transgenic organisms is part of the assessment of their environmental impact.

Question 3.9 *(Objectives 3.1, 3.2, 3.8 & 3.9)*

Using the EIA checklist given in Table 3.1 for guidance, assess the possible positive and negative environmental impacts of engineered baculoviruses if they were used to replace water-soluble, non-selective insecticides for control of herbivorous insects in horticultural crops growing on freely draining soils in a mainly arable area.

Objectives for Chapter 3

After completing Chapter 3, you should be able to:

3.1 Recall and use in their correct context the terms printed in **bold** in the text. (*Questions 3.1, 3.3 & 3.9*)

3.2 To describe the process, and recognize some of the strengths and weaknesses of Environmental Impact Analysis. (*Question 3.1*)

3.3 To recognize the role of ecological knowledge in Environmental Management Systems. (*Question 3.1*)

3.4 To evaluate evidence concerning the effects of a suggested pollutant. (*Questions 3.2 & 3.3*)

3.5 To recognize the importance of human activity in maintaining desired communities, and the changes in management imposed by economic factors. (*Questions 3.7 & 3.8*)

3.6 To use population dynamic models to assess harvesting regimes for exploited animal species, and to recognize the conflicts between conventional economic models and other considerations in determining how to harvest such species. (*Question 3.4*)

3.7 Given suitable data, to identify reasons for absence or poor performance of vegetation on derelict land, and to suggest methods of revegetation. (*Questions 3.5, 3.6 & 3.8*)

3.8 To consider some of the factors that affect the use of genetically modified organisms in the field. (*Question 3.9*)

References for Chapter 3

Aerts, R., Huiszoon, A., van Oostrum, J. H. A., van de Vijver, C. A. D. M. and Willems, J. H. (1995) The potential for heathland restoration on former arable land at a site in Drenthe, The Netherlands, *Journal of Applied Ecology*, **32**, 827–35.

Bradshaw, A. D. and Chadwick, M. J. (1980) *The Restoration of Land*, Blackwell.

Brenchley, W. E. and Adam, H. (1915) Recolonisation of land allowed to revert to natural conditions, *Journal of Ecology*, **3**, 193–210.

Brown, S. L., Chaney, R. L., Angle, J. S. and Baker, A. J. M. (1994) Phytoremediation potential of *Thlaspi caerulescens* and bladder campion for Zinc and Cadmium contaminated soil, *Journal of Environmental Quality*, **23**, 1151–57.

Clark, C.W. (1973) The economics of overexploitation, *Science*, **181**, 630–4.

Clutton Brock, T. H. and Lonergan, M. E. (1994) Culling regimes and sex ratio biases in Highland red deer, *Journal of Applied Ecology*, **21,** 521–27.

Department of the Environment/Welsh Office, (1989) *Environmental Assessment: a guide to the procedures*, HMSO, London.

Gambell, R. (1993) International management of whales and whaling; an historical review of the regulation of commercial and aboriginal subsistence whaling. *Arctic*, **46**, 97–107.

Glasson, J., Therivel, R. and Chadwick, A. (1994) *An Introduction to Environmental Impact Assessment*, UCL Press.

Hardin, G. (1965) *The Tragedy of the Commons, Science*, **162**, 1243–48

Department of the Environment (1992) *The UK Environment*, H.M.S.O.

Holdgate, M. W. (1994) Ecology, development and global policy, *Journal of Applied Ecology*, **31,** 210–11.

Hunt, D. and Johnson, C. (1995) *Environmental Management Systems, Principles and Practice*, McGraw-Hill.

ISO 14000 (1995) *Environmental Management Systems – General Guidelines on Principles, Systems and Supporting Techniques*. Committee Draft.

Morris, M. G., Thomas, J. A., Ward, L. K., Snazell, R. G., Pywell, R. F., Stevenson, M. J. and Webb, N. R. (1994) Re-creation of Early-successional Stages for Threatened Butterflies – an Ecological Engineering Approach, *Journal of Environmental Management*, **42**, 119–35.

Munn, R. E. (1979) *Environmental Impact Assessment: principles and procedures*, John Wiley, New York.

Nellerman, C. and Frogner, T. (1994) Spatial patterns of spruce defoliation: relation to acid deposition, critical loads and natural growth conditions in Norway, *Ambio*, **23**, 255–59.

Pigott, C. D. (1977) The scientific basis of practical conservation, *Proceedings of the Royal Society of London B*, **197**, 59–68.

Ratcliffe, D. A. (1980) *The Peregrine Falcon*, Poyser, Berkhamsted.

Rogan, W. J., Gladen, B. C., McKinney, J. D., Carreras, N., Hardy, P., Thullen, M., Tinglestad, J. and Tully, M. (1986) Neonatal effects of transplacental exposure to PCBs and DDE, *Journal of Paediatrics*, **109**, 335–41.

Smith, R. S. and Rushton, S. P. (1994) The effects of grazing management on the vegetation of mesotrophic (meadow) grassland in Northern England, *Journal of Applied Ecology*, **31**, 13–24.

Spellerberg, I. F. (1994) The biological content of environmental assessments, *Biologist*, **41**, 126–8.

Turner, B. L. II and Meyer, W. B. (1993) Environmental Change: The Human Factor, in: Mc Donnell, M. J. and Pickett, S. T. A. (eds) *Humans as Components of Ecosystems*, Springer Verlag, 40–50.

United Nations Economic Commission for Europe (1991) UN, Geneva.

van Elsas, J. D., Govaert, J. M. and van Veem, J. A. (1987) Transfer of plasmid pFT30 between bacilli in soil as influenced by bacterial population dynamics and soil conditions, *Soil Biology and Biochemistry*, **19**, 639–647.

World Commission for Environment and Development (1987) *Our Common Future*, Report of the 1987 World Commission for Environment and Development, Oxford University Press.

CONCLUSIONS FOR BOOK 5

So where does all this leave us, as professional, or would-be professional ecologists? We must accept our share in the processes which have affected the ecology of the planet. Turner and Meyer's 1993 model (Chapter 2) predicts the impact of humans on the global ecosystem as the product of population production and consumption: if you are a citizen of Western Europe, Japan or the USA, your contribution to production and consumption is disproportionately high. As an ecologist, what can you do about this? At a personal level, you should now be more aware of some of the ways that you directly affect ecological processes, through use of resources and discharge of materials into the environment. You should also be able to consider how your actions contribute to the wider use of resources by society as a whole, in producing the goods and services that you consume. Study of this Course should enable you to make some clearer decisions about the implications of your and others' actions – ways in which you can perhaps be more of a 'Green Consumer'. Don't imagine this is easy; study of this and the earlier Books should have made you critical of simplistic explanations of ecological phenomena and of humans' role in them. It may be tempting to rely on simple models as a guide to action, and it is certainly much easier to 'sell' these to a sceptical public when asked for advice.

Finally, we have to ask what aspects of global ecology should be of greatest concern and why. The difficulties here are well illustrated by the current interest in biodiversity. This may stem in part from a vivid metaphor coined by the Ehrlichs in 1981 (Chapter 2), the **'rivet popping' hypothesis**. According to this, each species in the world is like a single rivet in the structure of an aircraft. As each one is lost, so the structure of the aircraft is weakened, to the point where, once a critical number has been lost, the aircraft may lose structural integrity and crash. In contrast to this apocalyptic view, Brian Walker of the Commonwealth Scientific and Industrial Research Organisation in Australia suggested that most species are actually superfluous in ecological terms; they are more like **passengers** on the aeroplane than rivets. With the exception of a few key species, 'Aeroplane Earth' can lose many of its passengers without any serious effects.

This dichotomy of views obviously has important implications for policy. A meeting in California in 1994 attempted to review any experimental evidence which might favour one or other of the views concerning the importance of biodiversity. One example was work on artificial ecosystems in growth cabinets, conducted at Imperial College in the UK. By varying the numbers of species in these artificial systems, they produced the relationship between biomass accumulation and species number shown in Figure 3(i). Other workers have questioned the validity of this experiment since results using these species mixtures were not reproduced when different species mixtures were used. Despite this, the results are interesting as a contribution to the general argument.

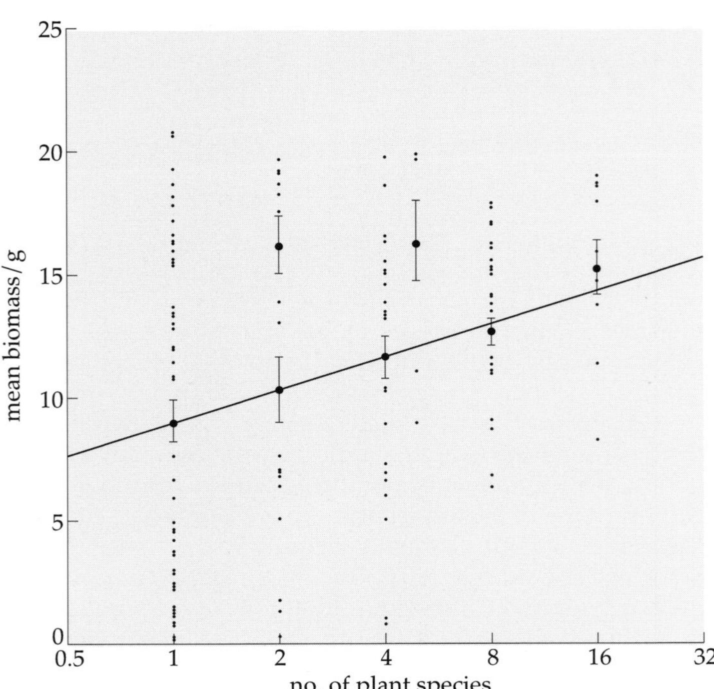

Figure 3(i) The relationship between number of plant species in a model ecosystem and the accumulation of biomass.

❑ What are the implications of the data on biomass accumulation?

■ Although there was considerable variation about the regression line, it appeared that increasing the number of plant species increased the accumulation of biomass.

Compared to agricultural practice in Europe and the USA, where near monocultures are used, this result may seem surprising. However, there is a widespread literature on multiple cropping from tropical conditions, which suggests that in many cases, increased accumulation can be realized in the field by **intercropping** plants of different architecture, growing season, etc. A secondary advantage claimed for intercropping is that the yields obtained may be more resilient in the face of variations in weather, etc., another aspect of the general diversity–stability debate.

The literature on multiple cropping suggests that biodiversity is at least useful under some circumstances. However, it is possible that the 'passenger' model is also true, once there is a reasonable number of passengers rather than just one or two. In agronomic experiments, there have rarely been reports of increased yields from assemblages of more than about five species. A comparison of the productivity of North American, European and Eastern Asian forests showed that all exhibited similar productivity, with 158, 106 and 876 tree and shrub species respectively.

So where does this leave the question of the value of biodiversity? There are two extreme reactions to the available data. One is the so-called **precautionary principle** which states that we should err on the side of caution, assume that loss of biodiversity could have serious effects on the planet, and do all we can to avoid it. The other extreme is propounded by some economists, who claim that human actions to protect other species will decrease **wealth creation**, and we will therefore be less able to counteract any deleterious effects that may occur in the future. If no deleterious effects occur, then we will all be better off anyway, so we win out whatever the results.

Deciding between these two models is not a scientific question, but it is one on which it is valuable for ecologists at least to ponder, to recognize the limitations of ecological knowledge and to seek to extend that knowledge.

❑ The following example is intended to give you an indication of the issues at stake and the scale of the financial considerations involved in decisions about biodiversity. Clear felling a given area of tropical forest will provide a logging company and local residents with an immediate cash benefit of $20 million and an annual income of $50 000 for at least five years. There is a 1 in 10 000 chance that a species exists in the forest which contains a pharmaceutical compound which would provide a market with a net value, after research costs, of $5 million per year for 10 years. Using this example, rehearse the ecological, economic and ethical arguments for and against clear felling areas of tropical forest.

■ Ecologically, the argument is that clear felling leads to loss of a particular community, and possibly to the extinction of species within that community. Subsequent changes in land use can lead to erosion or to other changes which have effects beyond the immediate area. How these are valued ethically is uncertain – does species loss matter?

The economic benefits are easier to evaluate, and standard accounting techniques can give an exact figure for the cash value of the activity. Assessing the economic value for the probability of losing a potential pharmaceutical is more difficult, and this again brings up the question of human attitudes. Is the chance of a future benefit worth more to the chooser than a sure immediate benefit? Is there an answer?

Summary

- The ecological impact of humans is considerable, and there is a need to develop criteria for measuring and controlling this.
- There is a general division between those who regard the preservation of biodiversity as important, and those who would prefer economic development.
- The currently available models of the role of different organisms, of biodiversity and other aspects of ecology are contentious, and are not yet able to be used convincingly in arguments about human activity.

ANSWERS TO QUESTIONS

CHAPTER 1

Question 1.1

The first and most obvious is the change in the species composition of the community, through cultivation and sowing of the crop, the use of herbicides and other methods, to produce something approaching a monospecific plant community. In addition, the genetic make-up of the dominant plant species has been changed by human intervention. The energy and nutrient flows of the arable field community show a substantial removal of carbon from the system, and high inputs of nutrients from outside the system. These changes have been associated with a decline in the avifauna of cereal fields, some of which may be reversed by the introduction of set-aside, which ensures that some fields carry naturally regenerated vegetation.

Question 1.2

Broadly, yes. Grain yields of the two new varieties followed the upward trend of the earlier data, but harvest index is similar to Norman and Hobbit, introduced five years earlier.

Question 1.3

Removing any input significantly reduced yield in all cases except for herbicides in 1986–87 and 1987–88. In two years, omitting fungicide had the biggest effect on yield, at least as large as the effect of removing all sprays. The between-year variation in yield was at least as great as the loss in yield from omitting any single input. The data suggest that fungicides are essential, but herbicides less so, which is rather different from the situation in the Boxworth trial.

Question 1.4

Weed cover is greater on set-aside than on cereal fields, and bird numbers increase with weed cover. This strongly suggests that weed seeds are being used directly as a source of feed.

Question 1.5

Not directly. The fisheries appeared to be able to support exploitation for quite long periods before the catches declined. This suggests that there may have been some other factors affecting the populations, which were possibly subject to cyclical variation in any case. It is interesting to note that the various sites also appeared to be out of phase in their cycles. However, it appeared that in the 1960s the herring population was seriously depleted, to the extent that the rate of fishing was unsustainable, and herring fishing was banned in that area. Subsequently, the stock is reported to have recovered somewhat. Disputes over fish stocks and their exploitation by different nations are still a regular feature of news bulletins.

Question 1.6

Mammals. However, the number of introduced alien species of higher plants and freshwater fish are of the same order of magnitude as native numbers. Introduced species would be likely to succeed if they were ones supported by humans, or those for which there were no predators. New Zealand had a very tiny mammal fauna prior to human introductions and so there would be no major predators on the introduced species.

Question 1.7

(a) The total number of species present in any one period shows a general increase, but the average number present is approximately 140. During the 3×10^6-year time-scale covered, there were a total of 332 extinctions, an average of one per 10 000 years, which is an average of 1% of the species in 14 000 years. This is within the range quoted earlier.

(b) The one relevant feature of the data is the large number (57) of extinctions of large mammals in period J, which ends with the first appearance of humans there.

(c) To decide whether this was evidence of a major effect of humans, it would first be necessary to determine what was the probability of the 57 extinctions occurring by chance. You would do this by looking at the *distribution* of the expected number of extinctions per 100 species per time interval. In this case, the distribution of extinctions per 100 species per time interval would probably be that known formally as the *Poisson distribution*. The probability of getting 57 or more out of 79 species extinct is given by estimating the *area* of the distribution to the right of this value, as a proportion of the total area (see the discussion of hypothesis testing in the *Project Guide*).

If the probability obtained from this distribution were suitably small, it would then be necessary to examine the palaeontological record to check what other events (e.g. climatic change) may have occurred during the same period, to see whether these could be responsible for the extinctions. It would also be necessary to determine whether similar large numbers of extinctions occurred in other areas at the same time without human incursion. The data suggest that the North American ecosystem had supported 40–80 large mammal species for a long period, so presumably there was some change in circumstances in period J which led to the sudden decline to 22 species. It is a matter of controversy whether these extinctions were due to human activity, but the case for human influence being a major factor is reasonably strong.

Question 1.8

There are two major reasons.

(i) The green cover is designed to take up soluble nitrogen forms from the soil, to reduce the chances of these leaching out of the soil.

(ii) Vegetation protects the surface of the soil from impact of raindrops, which could otherwise detach soil particles and erode them down slopes into watercourses.

A third virtue of green cover may be that it provides a food source for farmland birds, but this was not a specific intention of the requirement.

Question 1.9

Table A1 gives the data for permissible rates of application of each of the elements and the amounts dumped. Dividing the amount dumped by the permissible rate gives the minimum area required, in the fourth column. From this you can see that the largest area is 19.6 x 10^3 ha and is limited by the amount of copper in the sludge.

Table A1 Data for calculating minimum area needed for sludge dumping on farmland.

Element	Maximum application rate/kg ha^{-1} y^{-1}	Total mass of metal dumped/tonnes y^{-1}	Area required (mass dumped/maximum rate)/10^3 ha
zinc	15	288	19.2
copper	7.5	147	19.6
nickel	3	20.7	6.9
cadmium	0.15	2.06	13.7
lead	15	129	8.6
mercury	0.1	1.06	10.6

From Table A1, it appears that to have disposed of the sludge to farmland without exceeding the maximum rates of application of copper and zinc would have required about 20 000 ha. Since the spread material would require to be ploughed in, this land would have to be part of the arable area, and represents about 0.5% of the total arable area of the UK.

Question 1.10

The data for nitrogen differ little between the two States, with groundwater being the major source of nitrogen. This is presumably due mainly to leaching from agricultural soils, with the amount entering the waters approximately proportional to agricultural area in each case. For phosphorus, soil erosion is a much greater source in the former Federal Republic than in the former East Germany. Forestry, construction and inappropriate agricultural techniques can all lead to erosion. It is not possible to identify which was the most important of these. Direct inputs of phosphorus were important in both former States and these arise mainly from detergents.

Question 1.11

It appears that the pollen types associated with human activity (particularly Gramineae, *Rumex* and *Plantago*, first appeared at about the time of European settlement, but did not become very common until much later. The decline in pollen of the beech *Fagus grandifolia* appears to be associated with initial European settlement, but pollen of the chestnut *Castanea dentata* apparently increased after this date, until it declined very rapidly around the 10 cm level. This corresponds with an outbreak of chestnut blight, which destroyed most of the trees of this species in the period 1910–13.

Question 1.12

It is difficult to compare the two. Hannah *et al.* suggest that about 1.3% of the surface of the British Isles is either unaffected or minimally affected by humans. Superficially, it is possible that the heath and bog categories in the Countryside Survey are 'unaffected by humans' plus some of the moorland and mixed woodland. In total, these would sum to between 17 and 20% of the surface of mainland UK, which is much higher than Hannah's figure. However, we have already noted that many of the areas, such as moorland, are the result of human activity at an earlier time. Note also the discrepancies between the satellite and ground survey-based data for these types.

CHAPTER 2

Question 2.1

Although analogies can be drawn between human systems of agriculture and the activities of, for example, ants with their fungal gardens and plant associations (Book 1, Sections 1.5.5 and 1.7.3), humans are distinct from almost all larger omnivores in the extent to which they modify conditions for other organisms in order to secure a supply of food. Group hunting occurs in other animals (wolves, large cats) and some birds and primates use rudimentary tools, but humans are apparently the only species deliberately to use fire.

Question 2.2

Handling time represents the time spent dealing with prey, which would be reduced by humans acting in groups compared to individuals. Searching time would similarly be minimized by the passing of information within the group, and the use of weapons would increase the distance over which humans could attack prey. All these would enable humans to operate as effective predators, and would probably allow them to secure a larger proportion of the available resource than other non-specialized predators.

Humans do not have any specialized digestive functions akin to those of ruminants or termites, but they are able to select and process their food (milling, cooking, etc.) so that a high proportion is assimilable. One of the major factors affecting the $P : A$ ratio for large animals is loss of energy to keep warm. Human use of shelter and fire reduces this, so that a lower ratio of $P : A$ is achievable compared to other animals.

Question 2.3

Somatic energy is that energy which enters into human metabolic processes. Extra-somatic energy is absorbed as heat or via non-metabolic processes, such as the use of draught animals or machines.

Ambient forms of energy include solar radiation, or the combustion of recently formed biomass. These correspond to renewable sources. Fossil forms are primarily biomass from earlier geological materials, and are non-renewable.

Question 2.4

(a) See Table A2.

Table A2 Some comparative aspects of the energy flows in four different systems. Values are given as GJ ha^{-1}. (Answer to Question 2.4.)

	Tsembaga	Fyfield	Wiltshire	US maize
average net primary production	(361)	107	581	675
food energy produced for humans	0.73	(9.90)	48.30	102.90
food energy consumed by humans within the system	(0.73)	1.18	0.24	0.11
human work expended on food production	0.050	0.150	0.014	(0.010)
support energy used in food production	0.0	(very small)	18.7	35.2
ratio of food energy produced to total expenditure	14.60	66.00	2.58	2.92

(b) The highest ratio of food produced to work and support energy expended is shown by the historic Fyfield system.

Question 2.5

It does not represent recycling in any real sense. The only apparent 'recycling' of energy-containing compounds is via the wastes from human consumption (for which no data are given), but even here it is incorrect to speak of *recycling*. There is *transfer* of energy from one component of the system to another, but, overall, any ecosystem either dissipates its total energy income as heat, or stores a small proportion in biomass.

Question 2.6

The essential differences between Wiltshire and the US are in the amount of fertilizer used, which is higher for the US case, and in the proportion of primary production which is processed via animals. A substantial proportion of the primary production of cereals in Wiltshire and, significantly, *all* the utilized production from the lucerne, is consumed by animals, which have a trophic level efficiency of about 0.1. So, using forage legumes may save fertilizer use, and hence support energy use, compared to conventional forage feeding, but it still does not give as high an efficiency as would conventional cereal production if the cereal was consumed directly by humans. In practice, much of the cereal produced in the UK and USA is fed to livestock, so the calculation of efficiency is further complicated.

Question 2.7

The solar income represents $400 \times 3600 \times 12 \times 365$ joules or 6.3 GJ per square metre per annum. This is equivalent to 63 000 GJ per hectare per annum, so that the use of support energy is still relatively trivial compared to solar income.

Question 2.8

Your answer will obviously depend on your lifestyle, but the major demands for materials that we make are for foodstuffs (and indirectly for the resources needed to grow, process and transport them) and for fuel, to heat the house and to drive to work. To this must be added the resources needed to make those 'consumer durables' (i.e. things that wear out!) such as washing machines, cars, televisions and the paper which is used in this Book.

Relatively minor wastes are sewage and general household wastes, but major ones are the combustion products from cars and heating systems.

Question 2.9

From Table 2.3, copper reserves in 1950 were about 124×10^6 t, which would last 44 years at the then current rate of consumption. In 1991, reserves had risen to about 590×10^6 t, which should last about 55 years. Recycling of used copper and improved techniques of extraction from the ore, so that ores of a lower quality can be used, are two possible factors which may extend the life of reserves.

Question 2.10

In general, yes; traditional farmland could be regarded as an early successional stage, which has been replaced by an even more disturbed stage. So it would be expected that species adapted to this stage would be adversely affected.

Question 2.11

(a) There was no significant difference between the finite rates of increase of the two genotypes in cultivated soil, but the genetically engineered rape line had a significantly lower value of λ in at least one year in uncultivated soil. Rates of increase were lower in the uncultivated than the cultivated soil in all years.

(b) λ would have to exceed 1 for the genotype to expand its population.

(c) On the basis of this experiment, the transgenic line seems unlikely to become a weed, certainly no more so than the conventional line. However, any carryover of the herbicide-resistant line would be more serious than carryover of the conventional line if for any reason there was no approved herbicide available to control it.

Question 2.12

The two diagrams suggest that the rate of increase in population for Southern Asia will be considerably greater than for China, and that in both cases, the population age structure will change. For China, the proportion of adults in the 25- to 65-year-old age groups is projected to increase greatly, although there will be little increase in the under-20 population. For Southern Asia, the greatest proportional increase is projected to be in the 10- to 40-year-old groups. One implication of these differing age structures is that the total Southern Asian population will continue to increase for longer than that of China, since a higher proportion of the population will be of active reproductive age. However, this segment of the population is also potentially the most active economically, which could result in the desired birth rate declining rapidly. The effects of this economic activity on the ecology of the region will, of course, depend on the technology that is chosen to provide it.

Question 2.13

The data are consistent with the theory, since there was a decrease in both death rates and birth rates over the period. However, to conform to the model, the decline in birth rate should lag behind that in childhood mortality, and the exact time course of changes in the two variables is not given.

CHAPTER 3

Question 3.1

The exact answer will depend on the activity chosen, but as an example, consider the writing of this text. This is done on a word processor, either in an office at the University or at home, and paper copies are circulated to the Course Team at intervals. My initial analysis is given in Table A3 with some further detail for the relevant items in Table A4. It is a relatively low impact activity, the main effects arising from use of fuel and, to a lesser extent, paper. One consideration is the relative impact of working at home compared to the University office. This is heated whether or not I am using it, whereas my home is not heated during the day unless I am working there. Heating the house for a working day takes an extra 3–5 litres of oil. To balance this, working at home for a day saves the one litre of diesel oil used travelling and exhaust emissions generated.

Table A3 Listing of items affected by the activity of writing this text. Items marked with + or ++ are affected slightly or more seriously, 0 is no effect, ? is uncertain.

Item	Effect	Item	Effect
Air		*Water*	
global warming	++	oxygen demand	0
ozone layer	0	hydrocarbon spills	0
acid emissions	+	eutrophication	0
ground level ozone	+	hazardous substances	0
hazardous gases/fumes	0	hazardous organisms	0
smoke	0	acidification	0
radioactivity/radiation	0	thermal discharges	0
		radioactivity	0
Land		foaming, colour, litter	?
hazardous waste	0	taste	0
radioactive waste	0	water usage	+
non-hazardous waste	+	ecosystem disturbance	?
site contamination	0		
disturbance	0	*Nuisance*	
soil erosion	0	visual	0
		dust	0
Resource usage		odour	0
minerals/raw materials	0	noise, vibration	0
energy	+		
fuels	+		
stock exploitation	+		

Table A4 Notes on environmental effects.

Effect	Notes
global warming	carbon dioxide from fuel use, either for heating of home or transport
acid emissions	arising from fuel use
ground level ozone	possibly affected by emissions from transport
non-hazardous waste	paper from photocopies, drafts, etc.
energy	heating, transport
fuels	heating, transport
stock exploitation	paper use, but possibly less with use of word processor than handwritten drafts
foaming, colour, litter	paper discarded, plus possible discharges during paper manufacture
water usage	paper manufacture
ecosystem disturbance	timber production for paper?

Question 3.2

(a) The lizard *Mabuya striata* was sighted significantly less often in the sprayed area, and the numbers of other lizards sighted in these areas was also lower, but this effect was not significant. The proportion of *M. striata* decreased with increasing rates of spraying and hence other species formed a greater proportion of the reduced total number of lizards.

(b) Since lizards feed on insects, they would probably accumulate the DDT or DDE in their bodies if they ate sprayed insects, and these substances were found in the lizards. However, it appears that only *M. striata* is significantly affected by spraying. Birds feeding on the lizards would bioaccumulate the toxin, so the data are consistent with the earlier studies.

Question 3.3

The data are consistent with defoliation being associated with pollution by all three measured factors. The extent of defoliation does not appear to be associated with soil type, or with the expected productivity of the site, but is associated with low values of calcium, magnesium and buffering capacity in the soil. It is also associated with altitude, as suggested in the Forestry Commission study, but that study also noted that altitude and pollution load are correlated. The data are strongly suggestive of a link with pollution, but would need to be supported by appropriate physiological studies to be used as a basis for policy.

Question 3.4

(a) As the percentage cull of hinds increases from 0 to 24%, the equilibrium population of hinds more than one year old declines at an increasing rate to less than 200. The total population of stags over one year of age increases up to a peak of about 500 with a culling rate of 12–16%, and then declines relatively rapidly. Trophy stags, those of 5 years of age in the equilibrium population, do not vary greatly in numbers for culling rates between 6 and 20% of hinds, but appear to peak at around 70 for a culling rate around 16%.

(b) On the basis of the model given, a hind culling rate of 7% would not appear to be optimal; it would result in too high a population of hinds and consequently increased natural mortality.

(c) Figure 3.15 suggests that the optimum culling rate of hinds to produce the maximum number of trophy stags of five years old would be around 16%.

(d) The number of trophy stags in the equilibrium population varies only slightly across a wide range of culling rates, so the optimum is not very sensitive to variation in this. Thus, advising any rate within the range 6–20% would apparently give a similar number of trophy stags; if the model is correct, you could be reasonably confident in recommending any rate in this range. It would be useful to look at the *sensitivity* of the model to variation in its parameters, to be sure that the flat response to culling rate is not sensitive to any particular factor.

Question 3.5

(a) The question states that the mud has a high pH, which would restrict the availability of some nutrients, and it is largely anaerobic. If nutrient deficiencies alone restricted growth, then addition of nutrients (the shaded areas in Figure 3.19) should allow normal growth. This is not, however, the case. The desert saltgrass should be able to grow in anaerobic soils, but on mud alone, or with additions of straw, pine needles or glucose, it did not grow very well. Addition of paper pulp or sewage sludge produced shoot growth equal to the control but rhizome growth was only similar to control values in the paper pulp and sewage sludge treatments with added nutrients. It appears that some leachate from the pulp or sludge has a major influence on growth. Sewage sludge and paper pulp are both sources of finely divided organic matter; the beneficial effects may be due to microbial action on these materials, although the ineffectiveness of glucose, which should act as a microbial substrate, does not support this idea.

(b) Pragmatically, it appears that spreading sewage sludge and fragments of *Distichles* rhizomes on the mud surface ought to work, though it is not entirely clear why.

(c) The major limitation would almost certainly be the cost of the spreading. It is also unrecorded as to whether the *Distichles* sward survives for any length of time.

Question 3.6

(a) The amounts of zinc and cadmium are much higher in soil from site 3 than in the other two. Tomato yield is very significantly reduced in both soils 2 and 3 compared to soil 1, and is increased with increasing pH. The yield of *Thlaspi* is less affected, but also increases with pH except in the highest pH treatment on soil 3. The total amount of zinc taken up by the tomato is small, and is apparently unaffected by the amount in the soil. *Thlaspi* increases the amount it takes up per pot as the amount in the soil increases, although not in proportion. It also increases the amount of cadmium taken up as soil concentration increases, but the tomato takes up less from the higher levels.

(b) The quantities removed by the hyperaccumulator could be useful. Assuming that each pot contains around a kilogram of soil, then the rate of removal indicated in the best treatments would reduce the level in the soil by about 1% per harvest. This might be useful in some circumstances.

(c) Heavy metals are a common contaminant of urban sewage (Chapter 1, Section 1.5). Growing *Thlaspi* on soil where sewage had been spread would help to reduce the heavy metal burden if it were harvested and the metal extracted from the biomass.

Question 3.7

(a) Absence of grazing significantly reduced species richness compared to other treatments. Species diversity was lowest in the ungrazed treatment, but the difference was only significant between this and the 'normal' grazing treatment, which also significantly reduced biomass compared to the ungrazed and autumn grazed treatments. There were few consistent and significant differences between the grazing treatments.

(b) Grazing appears to be essential to maintain both diversity and richness, and generally, the traditional grazing regime was superior to either spring or autumn grazing alone.

Question 3.8

From the Table, organic matter, carbon and nutrient levels are higher in the uncultivated arable soil than in the heathland soil, and the C : P ratio is lower. There are no significant differences between the C : N ratios of the soil types. The difference in phosphorus level appears to be the biggest distinction, and this is supported by the changes in extractable phosphorus over time, where the heathland soil has a very low level compared to the arable soil.

(b) If low phosphorus levels are needed for *Calluna* heath to survive, then since topsoil removal does decrease phosphorus, it may be a valuable treatment.

(c) There is no seedbank of *Calluna* in the arable soil, so propagules of *Calluna* would have to be introduced.

Question 3.9

Table A5 reproduces the topic areas suggested for an Environmental Impact Assessment, and identifies those most likely to be relevant to the suggested comparison.

Table A5 Possible impacts of the baculovirus biopesticide and conventional water soluble form (✔ = some effect, ✕ = no effect, **?** = effect unknown).

Impact on:	**Baculovirus**	**Conventional pesticide**
land use, landscape and visual quality	✔	✔
geology, topography and soils	✔ (soil?)	✔
hydrology and water quality	✔	✔
air quality and climate	✕	✕
ecology; terrestrial and aquatic	✔	✔
noise	✕	✕
transport	✕	✕
socio-economic factors	?	?
interrelationships between effects	?	?

Of the effects listed in the Table, those on ecology and hydrology are probably the most important. Leaching of the conventional pesticide into water is probably a serious impact, and one which use of the baculovirus would eliminate if it were sufficiently effective in replacing the conventional material. Direct effects on the soil fauna should also be less with the baculovirus. It is possible that the baculovirus would also be more benign in its ecological effects on organisms in water courses if the conventional pesticide affects these, as seems highly likely. What is not clear ecologically is what other effects the baculovirus could have. Could there be transfer of genetic material from this into other organisms? Could its host specificity change, so that it attacks non-target species? Given its apparently low survival in the field, these impacts are unlikely, but it is difficult to put any precise probabilities on this.

On balance, the baculovirus appears to have less impact than the conventional pesticide. However, the evidence from the trials is that, at present, it is not a very effective pesticide. So using it would probably have negative economic consequences with increased damage to the crops from insects.

Acknowledgements

Grateful acknowledgement is made to the following sources for permission to reproduce material in this Book:

Cover photos Mike Dodd, Open University; *Figure 1* A. Brown (ed.) (1992) *The UK Environment*, Government Statistics Service © Crown copyright. Reproduced by permission of the Controller, HMSO; *Figure 1.2* R.A. Leigh and J.H. Stevenson (1993) 'Famous laboratories – Rothamsted Experimental Station', *Biologist* © Institute of Biology; *Figure 1.3* W.P. Davies and M.J. Gooding (1995) 'Developing lower-input wheat production systems' in Staniforth, A.R., *Agricultural Progress*, **70** © Agricultural Education Association; *Figure 1.4* J. Marshall (1992) in Greig-Smith, P., Frampton, G. and Hardy, A., *Pesticides, Cereal Farming and the Environment – The Boxtree Project*, MAFF © Crown copyright. Reproduced by permission of the Controller, HMSO; *Figure 1.7* L.J. Rew *et al.* (1992) 'Changes in vegetation composition and distribution within set-aside land', *Set-aside BCPC Monograph No. 50* © British Crop Protection Council; *Figure 1.8* G.R. Potts and N.J. Aebischer (1994) 'Population dynamics of the grey partridge *Perdix perdix* 1793–1993 …', *IBIS*, **137** © British Ornithologists' Union, Blackwell; *Figure 1.9* S. Tapper and J. France (1992) 'The National Game Bag Census – 1992 Season', *The Game Conservancy Review of 1992*, **24** © The Game Conservancy; *Figure 1.10* J. Wilson *et al.*, *Wasteland or Oasis? The use of set-aside by breeding and wintering birds*, British Wildlife, BBSRC-NERC Ecology and Behaviour Group; *Figures 1.11, 1.14* R. Hilborn (1990) in Turner, B. L. *et al.*, *The Earth as Transformed by Human Action*, Cambridge University Press; *Figure 1.16* B.J.L. Berry (1990) in Turner, B.L. *et al.*, *op. cit.*; *Figure 1.19* I. Douglas (1990) in Turner, B.L. *et al.*, *op. cit.*; *Figure 1.20* The Copper Development Association; *Figure 1.21* English China Clays Group; *Figure 1.22* W. Werner and H.-P. Wodsak (1995) 'The role of non-point nutrient sources in water pollution – present situation, countermeasures, outlook', *Water Science and Technology* © 1995 IAWQ, Pergamon; *Figure 1.24* Andrew Spackman; *Figure 1.25* D.R. Foster *et al.* 'Post settlement history of human land use and vegetation dynamics of a *Tsuga canadensis* woodlot in central New England', *Journal of Ecology*, **80** © British Ecological Society; *Figure 2.2* M.D. Coe (1964) 'The chinampas of Mexico', *Scientific American* © Scientific American Inc. All rights reserved; *Figures 2.9, 2.10* J.A. Thomas and M.G. Morris (1994) 'Patterns, mechanisms and rates of extinction among invertebrates in the United Kingdom', *Philosophical Transactions of the Royal Society of London*, **344** © Royal Society; *Figure 2.11* H.J. Rogers and H.C. Parkes (1995) 'Transgenic plants and the environment', *Journal of Experimental Botany*, **46** © Oxford University Press; *Figure 2.12* M.J. Crawley *et al.* (1993) 'Ecology of transgenic oilseed rape in natural habitats', *Nature*, **363** © Macmillan; *Figures 2.16, 2.17* W. Lutz (1993) 'Population: The dynamics of change', *Outlook on Agriculture*, **22** © CAB International; *Figure 3.1* J. Glasson, R. Therivel and A. Chadwick (1994) *Introduction to Environmental Impact Assessment: Principles and Procedures, Process, Practice and Prospects*, UCL Press Ltd; *Figure 3.2* D. Hunt and C. Johnson (1995) *Environmental Management Systems: Principles and Practice*, McGraw-Hill International (UK) Ltd; *Figure 3.3* D. A. Ratcliffe (1980) *The Peregrine Falcon*, Poyser, Berkhamsted; *Figure 3.4* D. A. Ratcliffe (1970) 'Changes attributable to pesticides in egg breakage frequency and eggshell thickness in some British birds', *Journal of Applied Ecology*, **7**, pp. 67–115, British Ecological Society, Blackwell; *Figures 3.5–3.7* D.J.A. Brown and K. Sadler (1981) 'The chemistry and fishery status of acid lakes in Norway', *Journal of Applied Ecology*, **18**, British Ecological Society, Blackwell; *Figures 3.8 and 3.9* I. Renberg, T. Korsman and N.J. Anderson (1993) 'A temporal perspective of lake acidification in Sweden', *Ambio*, **22**(5), Aug., Royal Swedish Academy of Sciences; *Figure 3.10* Special Topic Steering Committee (1991) *Effects of Atmospheric Pollutants on Forests and Crops,* Natural Environmental Research Council; *Figure 3.11* E.D. Schulze (1989) 'Air pollution and forest decline in a spruce (*Picea abies*) forest', *Science*, **244**, pp. 776–83, AAAS; *Figure 3.12* © ICI 1992; *Figure 3.13* R. J. Douthwaite and C.C.D. Tingle (1994) 'DDT in the Tropics', Chatham, UK, Natural Resources Institute; *Figure 3.15* T.M. Clutton Brock and M.E. Lonergan (1994) 'Culling regimes and sex ratio biases in highland deer', *Journal of Applied Ecology*, **21**, pp. 521–7, British Ecological Society, Blackwell; *Figures 3.16, 3.17* A.D. Bradshaw and M.J. Chadwick (1986) *The Restoration of Land*, Blackwell; *Figure 3.18* V.M. Palaniappan, R.H. Marrs and A.D. Bradshaw (1979) 'The effect of *Lupinus arboreus* on the nitrogen status of china clay wastes', *Journal of Applied Ecology*, **16**; *Figure 3.19* R.D. Fuller, E.D.P. Nelson and C.J. Richardson (1982) 'Reclamation of red mud (bauxite residues) using alkaline-tolerant grasses with organic amendments', *Journal of Environmental Quality*, **11**(3), American Society of Agronomy; *Figure 3.20* S.L. Brown *et al.* (1994) 'Phytoremediation potential of *Thlaspi caerulescens* and bladder campion ...', *Journal of Environmental Quality*, **23**, pp. 1151–57, American Society of Agronomy; *Figure 3.21* © Institute of Arable Crops Research, Rothamsted, Herts; *Figure 3.22* C.D. Pigett (1977) 'The scientific basis of practical conservation', *Proceedings of the Royal Society*, London, **197**, Royal Society; *Figures 3.23–3.26* M.G. Morris *et al.* (1994) 'Recreation of Early-successional stages for threatened butterflies – an ecological engineering approach', *Journal of Environmental Management*, **42**, pp. 119–35, Academic Press; *Figure 3.27* R. Aerts *et al.* (1990) 'The potential for heathland restoration on formerly arable land at a site in Drenthe, The Netherlands', *Journal of Applied Ecology*, **32**, pp. 827–35, British Ecological Society, Blackwell; *Figure 3.28* J.S. Cory (1994) 'First field trial of a genetically improved baculovirus insecticide', NERC News, July, NERC; *Figure 3.29* S. Naeem *et al.* (1995) 'Empirical evidence that declining species diversity may alter the performance of terrestrial ecosystems', *Philosophical Transactions of the Royal Society of London*, **B 347**, pp. 249–62, Royal Society.

INDEX

Entries and page numbers in **bold type** refer to key words which are printed in **bold** in the text. Pages indicated in *italics* refer to a figure or caption.